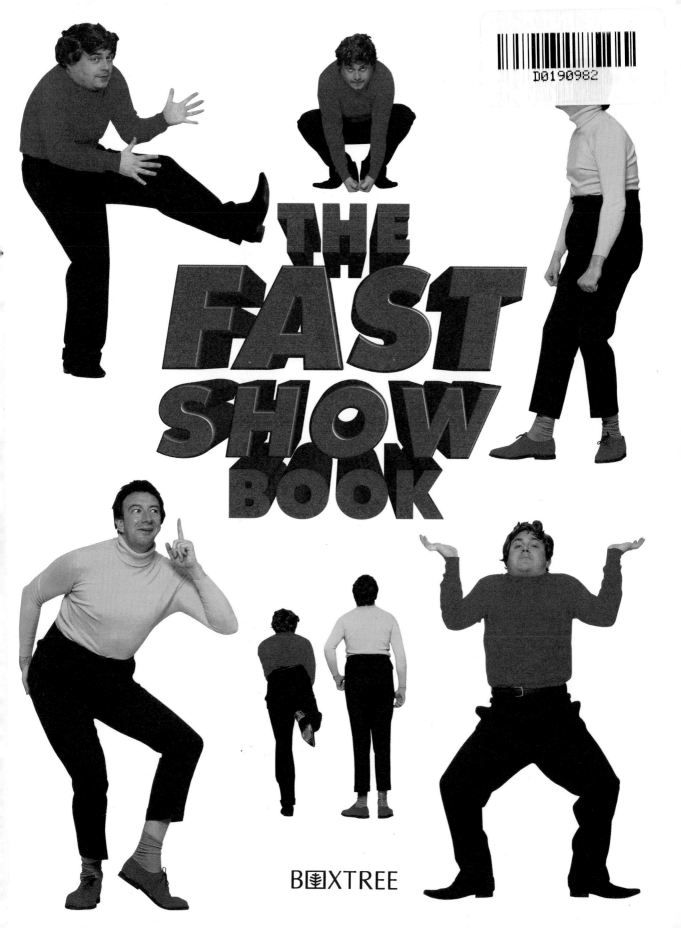

THE FAST SHOW BOOK

BⓇXTREE

B🌿XTREE

First published in the UK in 1996 by BOXTREE
an imprint of Macmillan Publishers Ltd
25 Eccleston Place, London SW1W 9NF

Associated companies throughout the world

ISBN 0 7522 2267 8

9 8 7 6 5 4 3 2 1

A CIP catalogue record for this book is available from the British Library

Design by Dan Newman
Principal photography by Paul Postle

Printed and bound in the UK by Cambus Litho Ltd, East Kilbride

Photo credits
Paul Postle: *Cover:* Jazz Club, Micky Disco, Different With Boys, Roy, Ron Manager, Denzil Dexter, Suit You, Patrick Nice, Poula Fisch, Brilliant, Renee, Competitive Dad, Janine; pp.1, 3, 6, 9, 12, 16, 17, 21, 26, 30, 31, 40, 42, 43, 48, 49, 55, 56, 57, 61, 64, tl 66, 68, 69, 70, 71, 72, 73, 74, br75, 76, 77, 78, 79, 86, 87, 90, *pp.94-95:* Poula, Janine, Roy & Renee, Denzil Dexter, Jazz Club, Chris Cockney, Brilliant, Billy Bleach, Competitive Dad, Get Me Coat, Patrick Nice, Ain't Seen Me, DWB, Insecure Woman, Ron Manager. **Ian Garlick:** pp.25, 41, 67, 80-81. **Tim Hill:** pp.24, 88-89. **Matthew May:** pp.16-17, 84-85. **Hulton Getty:** p.26. **Ronald Grant Archive:** 'Filming' pp.59, 60. **The Image Bank:** p.32. **People In Pictures:** 'Nun' p.45. **MPC Ltd:** pp.92, 93. **Colin Dawson Associates:** 'Off Road' pp.36, 37, 38, 39. **Jamie:** *Cover:* Ted, Simon Off Road, Unlucky Alf, Ralph; pp.4, 10, 14, 62, 63, *pp.94-95:* Crap Croupier, Off Road, Gideon Soames, Ted, Unlucky Alf. Tommy Cockles picture p.95 courtesy Avalon Ltd.

The following photographs copyright © British Broadcasting Corporation. Licensed by BBC Worldwide Ltd. *Cover:* Bob Fleming, Jesse's Diets; pp.27, 28, 36, 37, 54, 58, 60, tr 63, 66, br 74, cl 75, 82, 83; *pp.94-95:* Ralph, Bob Fleming, Geoffrey Norman, Jesse, Medieval Woman.

Contributors

Written by Charlie Higson & Paul Whitehouse with David Cummings

AND Caroline Aherne, Arabella Weir, Mark Williams, Simon Day,
John Thomson, Craig Cash, Henry Normal and Fiona Looney

Thanks to:

Director types: Mark Mylod, John Birkin, Sid Roberson
and Arch Dyson

Writer types: Graham Linehan, Arthur Mathews, Richard Preddy
and Gary Howe

Actor types: Paul Shearer, Robin Driscoll, Felix Dexter
and Colin McFarland

Costume Design: Annie Hardinge. Thanks to Sarah Burnes,
Natalie Rogers and Chris at Carlo Manzi's

Make-up and wigs: Jane Walker, Jayne Buxton and Kim Dewer

Original photography: Paul Postle, Jamie, Ian Garlick,
Tim Hill, Matthew May, Jake Lingwood and Guillaume Mustaars

Illustrations: Paul Campbell, Liz Watkins,
Dan Newman and Charlie Higson

Extras: Philip & Michael, Craig, Natalie, Art Young,
Tim Lawson and the staff of Esprit, Putney

Also thanks to Alexandra Cann, Samantha Ford, Adrian Sington,
Sarah Bennie, designer Dan Newman and editor Jake Lingwood.
Cheers

Introduction

Congratulations! You are the owner of the Fast Show Book. Now, if you're anything like me, I expect you've often wondered just how exactly a book is made. So, let's go now on a journey of discovery into the world of book manufacturing. But not just any book, this book, the Fast Show Book which you are holding in your hands. How did it get there? Well, as you can see it is *printed* on *paper*. Hang on, that's a bit obvious, isn't it? Well yes, but these days we're rather used to taking things for granted, aren't we. How much do we really know about that stuff that we write shopping lists on, that we read the daily news off of, that we wrap our chips in? 'Okay, tell me some more,' I can hear you saying. Well, paper was invented by the Chinese in the second century AD. It was originally made from pulped rags or plant fibres. Unfortunately, it was another five hundred years before anyone invented writing, so the unused paper presented quite a fire hazard. That's why the Chinese also invented kites; it was felt that the paper was safer up in the air out of harm's way. It was introduced into medieval Europe by the Moors, where it quickly superseded parchment, and contributed to the Great Fire of London.

From the nineteenth century, wood pulp or cellulose has been the main ingredient of paper. However, the use of plant fibres (such as esparto grass) and rags continues, especially for paper which needs to be strong or of high quality. Fortunately, that's not the case with this book, which will quickly fall apart if you actually attempt to read it. In a modern paper mill, machines cut wood* into chips, which are then mixed and cooked into a pulp. Watch out Jarvis Cocker! Heavy rollers press the pulp into a thin sheet and squeeze out excess water. Hot rollers then dry the paper, which is stored in huge reels. Well, we feel pretty confident that we know a bit more about our misunderstood friend paper now, don't we? 'Hang on though,' I bet you're saying, 'we need to know something about printing.' *No problem!* as the young people say. The oldest form of printing is the letterpress. The wooden handpress was superseded in 1795 by the first all-metal press, known as the *Stanhope*. Nowadays, typesetting is done quickly and efficiently on a computer. The Fast Show Book was printed by a firm in Glasgow, Scotland and delivered by *lorry* to Boxtree's warehouse in Littlehampton, on the Sussex coast. So the book has travelled the length of Great Britain even before it goes on sale. Fancy that! The warehouse in Littlehampton is called Littlehampton Book Services, or LBS as it is known in the trade (pick up a book in a shop and say 'Is this from LBS?' and the staff will think you're a real pro). If the book is bound for W.H. Smith, it must next travel to their warehouse in Swindon. With smaller booksellers and individual branches, the books are delivered by a parcel firm such as Securicor. The books are delivered in a variety of pack sizes, containing ten, twenty or more books, according to the order from the bookshop For a really large order, the books are delivered in crates. The Fast Show Book is very *popular* so it was probably delivered in a crate. Just think of that! Once the book is in a shop, the retailer can draw attention to it by displaying it in a *dump-bin*. A dump-bin is one of those large cardboard displays that are designed to catch the eye and let the customer know about a book. Did you see the dump-bin for The Fast Show Book? Whether or not a dump-bin is used is a decision made by *the marketing manager*. The strategic tools of the marketing manager are the product, its price, its channels of distribution, and its promotion (advertising and personal selling). These four tools are known as the *marketing mix*. The marketing manager combines them into strategies that will produce profitable sales. What, you may be asking, *are* profitable sales Well, let us assume that the cost of producing The Fast Show Book and getting it into the shops is X. Now, imagine that the price of the book is Y. If we subtract X from Y we get Z. Z represents the profit from a sale, andprofitable sales are when that happens more than once. Anyone wishing to know a bit more on this subject should buy a book called 'Marketing and Profit: Strategies and Planning' by Thomas Dixon, price

(cont. p 97)

* *Several acres of tropical rainforest have been felled in the production of this book.*

Flat 17
Norbury Towers
Rochdale

Dear Noel (Gallagher)

I think you're really great - you are the best. You are by far the greatest songwriter in Oasis.

I know Liam is better looking than you and everyone likes him best but I like you. I love the way you never try and talk posh just because you're famous like Dave Bowie.

Another thing, I know everyone takes the piss makes fun of your eyebrows but they wouldn't bother me. They look like love-catterpillars above your eyes of sparkling blue.

Do you know what's weird - when I heard Wonderwall I couldn't help going straight out wondering round Rochdale and then sitting on a wall. I know I'm not the only one to say this.

Please carry on writing those brilliant songs like 'don't look back in anger', 'Shakermaker', 'Supersonic', ect.

People say you sound just like the Beatles. I'd take this as a compliment if I were you. It never did them any harm.

I don't believe that anyone feels the way I do about now (do you get it - your lyrics).

Luv and stuff

Janine Carr (FAN)

I'm mad for it, me!

PS. Your Liam can read this if he wants to, but cover up the bit about him.

HAVE YOU SEEN THIS MAN?

This character has no visible income and no fixed address. He roams around sleeping rough or staying with sympathisers. He is usually accompanied by a gang of twelve cronies who do whatever he tells them. Do you know him? Have you seen him? If you do, don't hesitate to be a have-a-go-hero. He is not armed and dangerous, in fact he lives by the doctrine of turning the other cheek. Yes, he is our Lord Jesus Christ and a substantial reward is offered to anyone finding him – The reward of life everlasting in God's holy kingdom! Hallelujah! Christ is risen!

Distributed by The Organization Of Christian Coppers.

"Football, in the park, you know, where it belongs, not in the stadium, or is it stadia? Mm, isn't it? Mind you, some of these Italian ones are very impressive, aren't they? The whole local community's built round them, isnt it? But, small boys, where they belong, in the park, not in the stadiums, or is it stadia? Let's not go down that road

RON MANAGER'S PARK IN A BOX

SUITABLE FOR CHILDREN OF ALL AGES – FROM 6 TO 96! FOR 2 TO 22 PLAYERS

GAME INCLUDES:
- **Rules**
- **Dice**
- **Jumpers for goal posts**
- **Small boys**
- **Dog's muck**
- **Ball**
- **Parkie**
- **Mummy calling you in for tea**
- **The funny man who's always in the park**
- **Crisps**
- **Rush goalie**
- **Fence to lose ball over**
- **Flat ball**
- **Wasps**
- **Small girl who wants to join in**
- **Big boys who come and nick your ball**
- **Box of matches to set fire to things (insects, bins, leaves, parkie's hut. etc)**

again, shall we? No, small boys in the park, jumpers for goal posts, enduring image, like my own childhood, endless summer days, piles of frosty leaves in the autumn, dog's muck in the leaves, of course, sometimes a dead body, always found by dog-walkers. Where would the police be without men walking their dogs? They'd never find a single body, would they? But, er, yes, mm, my game, in a box, in it, isn't it? There. There it is. Um, Ron Manager's Park In A Box... Parklife! Blur, yes it's all a blur, well, it is to me, anyway..."

CRAP CROUPIERS GAMBLING TIPS

SYSTEM 1: LUCK BE A LADY

Many people will say things like "There's only one winner in this game and that's the bank". Or "The only people making money are the casinos". The people that tell you these things are telling you the truth. But let's not let these kind of killjoy comments worry us. All right, I've seen many a man totally ruined by the pull of the table, but if you can't stand the heat get out of the kitchen, the casino, no, don't get out of the casino, stay in it, because sheer luck can make you a millionaire. Yes, with my 'Luck be a Lady' system, based entirely on luck, you're on your way to beating the very people I work for. (Keep it quiet though, won't you?) Yes, what could be simpler? All you have to do is go to a casino and bet a large amount of money (it helps if you've got a couple of bob) on *any* game, that's right! ANY Game! Then sit back and let Lady Luck work her magic. The money will literally pour in.*

SYSTEM 2: IT'S ALL IN THE CARDS

The main problem with card-based games is that you never know what any of the cards are, since, when you've been a croupier as long as I have, you'll notice that the numbers and suits are printed only on one side. This is a trick thought up by the casino owners to make beating them much harder. But you can beat the odds by simply marking the cards in

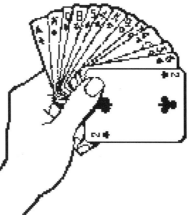

a way that is invisible to the naked eye. The best way to do this is to break into the card-making factory, Waddingtons, for example, and tamper with the actual printing plates. You will obviously need the help of a skilled printer, but there's dozens of them in the Yellow Pages. Of course, you'll have to split your winnings, but in any game you've got to speculate to accumulate. The changes you make to the cards will only be visible through special glasses, or contact lenses, and for this you will need the help of a qualified optician, who, like the printer will need to be in in on the deal, I suppose, so you'll lose a couple of bob there, too. (Also, make sure the optician isn't an undercover police optician, because, strictly speaking, the whole thing is illegal.) All right, so it sounds complicated, but it can be devastatingly effective if carried out properly, I should think.

SYSTEM 3: FOOLPROOF ROULETTE

People are always asking me if I have a system for winning at roulette. Well, you don't work the tables for as long as I have without picking up a thing or two. Like chips off the floor. Mind you I don't drop them as often as I used to. I've found I can keep my eye on what's going on at the table if I don't drop things on the floor. That's rule number one for a croupier: keep an eye on the table. A handy tip for any youngster reading this. Anyway, with all my experience, I reckon I've spotted the loophole that could have casino owners crapping themselves. Literally.

So here goes. It is a system that is so simple, it's beautiful. It's a work of art. it gives me the horn. The roulette table has a square you can bet on for an odd number, and a square you can bet on for an even number. Here's the tip: bet on both squares. That way you can't lose. Why no-one has spotted it is beyond me.

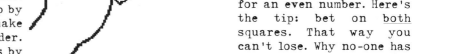

* Of course you might experience a run of bad luck, but that's just bad luck, you can't blame me for that. I'm just a guiding hand, not the be-all and end-all.

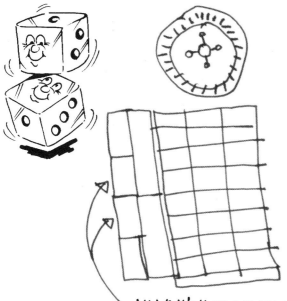

I think it's these ones you want

SYSTEM 4: REALLY FOOLPROOF ROULETTE

I've had problems with the above system. Some bloody nit-pickers claim that it doesn't work. You must be doing something wrong, that's all I can say. Go back and read the instructions carefully, then try again. Here's another system that is foolproof. You need to be holding quite a few chips to start with to work this one but believe me, it pays off every single time.

There are thirty-six numbers on a roulette wheel, so get yourself thirty-six chips. Can you guess what's coming? That's right! You bet on every single number. It's child's play! "But hang on a minute," I can hear you saying, "there's a hitch." I know, I know. Casinos won't allow a punter to bet on all the numbers at once because, by and large, they prefer you to lose. So you need to be a little bit crafty, a little bit subtle. What you do is get a syndicate together. Go to the casino with thirty-five of your mates, and each of you bet on a different number. Do it casually, though, 'cos if the casino smells a rat, you'll be out on your arse. Anyway, once you've got the bets on, one of you has to win. Then all of you leave, and nobody's any the wiser. The winner gets the drinks in for the other thirty-five and you celebrate your good fortune. Have one on me.

LETTERS

Dear Crap Croupier,
  do you think that film Rain Man was realistic? You remember, it's the one with Tom Cruise and Dustin Hoffman. They are brothers and Dustin Hoffman is artistic. There's a scene set in a casino where they win money before getting slung out.

Of course it's not realistic: if Dustin Hoffman was that thick, how on earth could he remember all them cards?

Dear Crap Croupier,
  soft hands at blackjack always confuse me. Sometimes I hit, sometimes I double down, but always I wonder if i've made the right move. This is especially true of the following hands: A2 vs. a dealer's five; A3 vs. the dealer's three; and A7 vs. the dealer's six and seven. What are the right moves and why are they the right moves?

Sorry mate, I've no idea.

Just before I go, I've one more tip to pass on. It's not a system, just a way of working the angles in your favour. When betting on odds or evens at the roulette table, bide your time for a bit. Watch how the run of play is going. If, for example, an odd number comes up nine times in a row, shove all your money on evens for the next bet. it's got to come up, hasn't it? It's a mathematical certainty.

You might wonder why I should share my tips with you. Well, ordinarily I wouldn't, but I've been having some bloody awful luck on the gee-gees recently and the publishers of this book are throwing a few bob my way. Mind you, they made me get this copied down the road, 2000 copies at 3p a time - so that's almost, what, seventeen quid I've spent on this. No. Thirty? Thirty-five? About that.

The **Philip Karlsberg** work-out system

When undergoing any course of physical exercise it is vital to keep up the level of fluids in the body. As we exercise, we sweat, our blood thickens and vital minerals and salts are lost. To counter the loss of fluids, we recommend an Isotonic drink sipped at regular intervals. You can buy these drinks in the shops, but they are vastly over-priced for what they are. It is quick and easy to mix up your own formula at home. Below is a simple recipe for a nutritious beverage.

0.25 litre mineral water
0.25 litre cranberry juice
Table spoon low-fat natural yoghurt
1 teaspoon of guarana extract (available from most chemists and health food shops)
Pinch of salt.
A banana
1 bottle vodka (or similar)
2 soluble aspirin

Whisk it all together in a blender and put it in a plastic bottle so that nobody can accuse you of being pissed, which you aren't, obviously.

1 WARM UP
Sway gently on your feet. Good for lymph drainage and circulation

2 STRETCHING
Extend one arm forwards, then lean back and point the arm upwards. Repeat until you feel fully relaxed.

3 ADD FLUIDS Very important.

4 **BICEP CURL** Hold arms at side with a suitable weight in your hand. A can of lager is about right for starters, the more experienced should attempt a duty free litre of vodka. Repeat eight times or until your four pack is gone.

5 **ADD FLUIDS**

6 **THE STAGGER** Collapse slowly sideways, moving your legs at the last moment to support your weight. It is important not to let anyone think that you are falling over, as this might lead them to believe that you are pissed, which, of course, you're not. Continue right across the floor and into the wall, then slowly slide down until you are sitting on the floor.

7 **ADD FLUIDS**

8 **SEATED BICEP CURL**

9 **WARM DOWN** Just as important as warming up. Relax in a prone position with your eyes shut, mouth open. Make sure you are lying on top of one of your arms so that it goes dead. Stay like this for at least six hours and you will feel refreshed, invigorated and ready for another session. In the unlikely event of any pain, dizziness or headaches, consult your local off-licence.

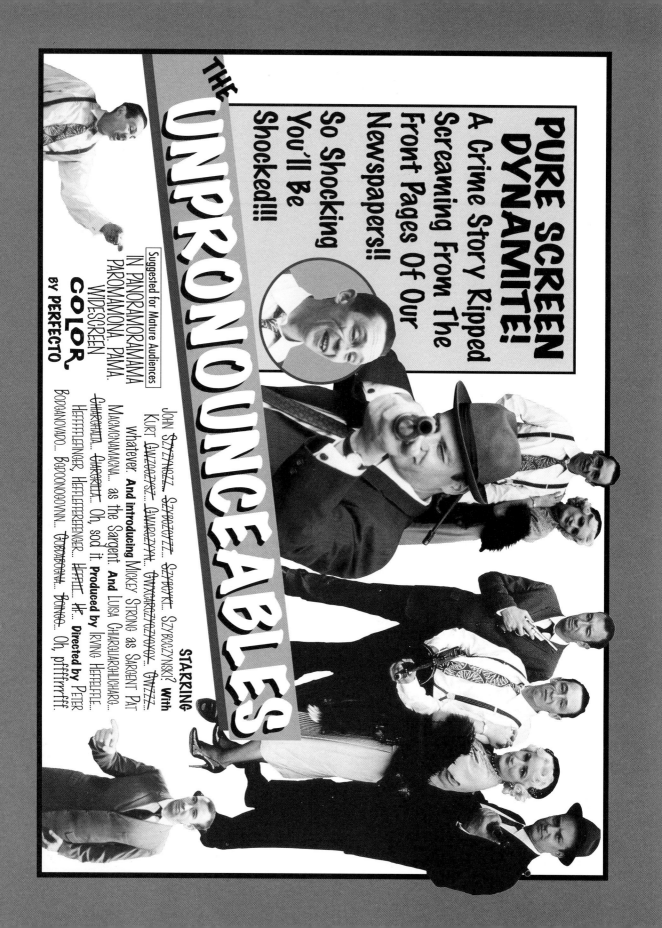

Growing & Preparing Herbs

CRESS (*Lepidum sativum*)
A lovely little wild, tearaway plant that needs no encouragement whatsoever. She's a most rewarding little salad herb, and you'll find yourself coming back to her again and again, each time begging for more.

ROSEMARY (*Rosmarinus officinalis*)
A difficult one, rosemary. Shy and slow to develop, she needs a lot of coaxing before she comes good. Worth the extra effort when she explodes in your mouth.

OREGANO (*Origanum vulgare*)
A great favourite with enthusiasts of all persuasions, oregano is a traditional plant; hardy and reliable, but she does feel the cold, so treat her gently in the mornings when she's at her most vulnerable. Prune her hard.

CORIANDER (*Coriandrum sativum*)
Full of Eastern promise, but sadly she doesn't always make good on that promise. A temperamental plant, a rampant, hot little minx who needs to be shown who's boss. Keep her in check with regular shaving.

CHIVES (*Allium schoenoprasum*)
One of the prettiest herbs in any garden, her bobbing, nodding head can often make the whole plant go down. She likes it hard up against a wall, where keeping erect isn't a problem.

FENNEL (*Foeniculum vulgare*)
Easy to recognise by its distinctive green fringe; almost like she's wearing a little dress with a short, tight skirt. Likes full sun and performs exceptionally well on moist evenings.

BASIL (*Ocimum basilicum*)
You'll never forget basil's pungent smell – I sometimes find it takes days to get it off my fingers. A tough, hardy plant that enjoys deep soil and plenty of dirt.

PARSLEY (*Petroselinum crispum*)
This little lass can cause problems for even the most experienced grower. Her delicate, nubile buds should be quite pert when she's ripe, but if you don't take her immediately, she's liable to grow tough and sullen. Pull her when she's very young.

SORREL (*Rumex acetosa*)
Easy to grow, not so easy to control; but she'll put on quite a show for you once you've given her a firm hand. Needs a lot of discipline, and may need occasional spraying. A pleasant taste, if a little tart.

MINT (*Mentha*)
A tricky one, is mint. Without constant attention, she'll spread – this lass really likes to be on top in any garden. Still, she's eager to please; slash into her regularly and she'll oblige with a lovely display.

CHERVIL (*Anthriscus cerefolium*)
Quick to come up, and keen to show herself to you, chervil responds to a light fingering, but this frisky lady can give you the runaround if you let her spread too far.

TARRAGON (*Artemisia dracunculus*)
You'll never forget your first taste of tarragon. She bursts into life on the tongue and performs like a real professional. Treat her mean and keep her keen.

DILL (*Anethum graveolens*)
A sly, truculent, lazy plant that demands a huge effort for very little return. Personally, after a number of bad experiences with dill, I've decided she's just not worth bothering with. A teasing little bitch.

CARROTS
Rampant, thrusting, look like big cocks.

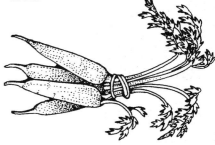

Jazz Club
choice cuts...

Jazz Club

20 choice cuts selected by Louis Balfour

Disc 1

1 **Neal Spender's Return of Tomorrow** Crimson Dawn
2 **The Dave Wilson Trio** In your clock*
3 **Monumental X** Legslider
4 **Donald Strong and his Jazz Tendency** Portrait of Mary
5 **Click Track** Doctor Mohair
6 **Lokoja Jo Tangana Featuring Baldman** Hairy Part 2
7 **Buddy Freep** The Fidget*
8 **Steve Cran's Re-Invention** Logical Rising
9 **Mama Thesis and the Jazz Babies with Papa's Full House** One Two She's Blue, Three Four That's Jazz
10 **Log On** Spiritual Hard Drive

Disc 2

1 **Hare Worth:** Tantric Jam
2 **Smack** No bare foot man gonna sell me my dinner (it's quarter to two)
3 **The Petey Young Trumpet Ensemble** Jazz Off!*
4 **Third and Broadway** Riffing for my Cat*
5 **Percy Hersh's Meltdown** We aint got none
6. **Bronx Cheer** Guitar Souffle
7 **Wilderness** Up jazz creek without a paddle
8 **Baloney** Elegy For Ken Smith
9 **Luckyman** I've got the Horn... (and yes, I can blow it)
10 **The Louis Balfour Quintet** Mmm, nice

9 780399 230332

"Hello, and welcome to Jazz Club – the album. Nice. Selecting these twenty tracks for you really was about the most enjoyable job I've ever had. Really! Jazz! Wonderful! Inevitably, restrictions of time and space means that after much soul searching (or should that be jazz searching?) I've had to leave out some favourites. Shame. But I do hope that these tracks build up a meaningful portrait of the wide world of jazz, ancient and modern. Nice. Wonderful."

The Dave Wilson Trio
In your clock
This was recorded at the legendary Sam Buttface Dyson sessions in the Blue Moon Records recording studio in New York on the 4th of July 1956 at roughly 3.27p.m. Nice. This is the second take, not the version which appeared on the album *Clockin' On* (Blue Moon BMR 3456) which was the third take. This version features an unexpected dropped suspended fourth in the turnaround from pianist Charlie Tree which led to a furious argument with Wilson which can be heard in the background of Bunny Lewinski's typically aposite saxaphone solo. I actually prefer this version with its bridge-fill-bridge-fill-two step tighten down structure leading to the last almost salsa-like push in the coda. Odd! Melodramatic? But wonderful.

Smack
No bare foot man gonna sell me my dinner (it's quarter to two)
No rules, no short change, just Hornfinger at his infuriating best. Awesome.

Percy Hersh's Meltdown
We aint got none
This features the definitive Meltdown line up of Colin 'Bateman' Bates on trumpet, Rolph Pitchford on drums, Artie Wobbler Smith on tenor, Hootie Dubbins on bass and, of course, Percy himself on Piano. Nice. Listening to this 1968 version recently I was once again overwhelmed by Percy's triumphant and cataclysmic solo with its rapid group of descending dactyls modulating from E minor to B flat incorporating a two beat suspended time change rotating through A, A, B and B, A, B, it vibrates, paraphrases, edits, echoes, and finally moves up a minor third as Percy seamlessly weaves in snatches of other songs: *Take the A train*, *Only You* and *Donald Where's Your Troosers*. Nice. In lesser hands this might be a mess, but not with Percy at the helm and Rolph teasing the rhythmic sructure into pastures new. Frightening but wonderful.

Monumental X
Legslider
Inspired by Reek Neddy's 1940s novelty hit *Foot Up*, Monumental X here turn the song inside out, make it jump through hoops and generally transform it into something strange and wonderful. Mmm. The typically startling and buoyant solo work from Fare Kula Ferret Musselman III is as ever supported by the rock solid and sadly under-rated rhythm section of Clam and Dave Plank. Keep an ear open also for Jacques P'estelle, Jesus Da Gralla and Dutch Max a-huffin' and a-puffin'- and a-stewin' up a storm of brass in the corner. Nice.

Wilderness
Up jazz creek without a paddle
The Reverend Blow's delightful take on this light jazz standard is an easy-pleasy classic which should never be far from anyone's turntable. Nice. This typically, airy, frothy confection was recorded just before the Reverend was arrested for income tax evasion, drug smuggling, armed robbery and wife beating. Wonderful. The distinctive bass playing comes courtesy of Mustafah Ben Kaleed, aka Sergeant Paddy McClussky of the NYPD who for fifteen years years went 'jazz undercover' in an attempt to track down the wily reverend.

IMP Academy Manuscript

The FULL TREATMENT

SPORTS DAY REPORT

The school sports day on July 1st was on the whole a huge success. Enthusiastic support was given by many parents, somewhat over-enthusiastic support was given by Toby Johnstone's father, Simon. His shouts of "Call that running?" and "Nobody remembers a loser" perhaps didn't help Toby's efforts in the 200 metres and caused him to finish a disappointing last. Toby's dad then insisted on joining in the 400 metres, even though sports master Ted Lobbster tried to explain that the events were really just for the chidren. "They've got to learn," Mister Johnstone told him. "Sport was invented as a preparation for war. You're not telling me adults don't join in warfare?" When Mr Lobbster tried to point out that the sports day was just for fun Mr Johnstone replied that there was no point in having a sports day if it wasn't conducted properly, at which point he started his warm-up following the Canadian Air Force exercize programme. He was finally persuaded to take his position on the blocks and the race could start. Toby's dad didn't do well in the race after one of his sandals fell off, and he was beaten into third place by school running champions Ryan Holder and Dale Forrester. He then insisted on urine samples being taken from the boys and accused them of mis-using anabolic steroids. The final result of the race is still unconfimred, pending the outcome of the injunctions Toby's father's solicitors have served against us. Ryan and Dale were considerably upset by proceedings and withdrew in tears from the final race, the 100 metres sprint, which was won easily by Toby's dad.

▲ IT'S A RECORD! SIMON JOHN-STONE WINS THE 100 METRES SPRINT

▼ WELL DONE! SPORTS MASTER TED LOBBSTER AWARDS SIMON JOHNSTONE THE WALTER HERTZ SPRINT TROPHY.

▲ IN TRIUMPHANT MOOD. TOBY'S DAD <u>AGAIN</u>

Aren't pelicans BRILLIANT? I mean how do they fit

all them fish in their gobs? Well they've got an big flap of loose skin, right, on the

underside of their bills, that's

you know, but sharks... brilliant... scary, but brilliant. End of story.

how. Fantastic! And aren't sharks brilliant, dolphins are alright, bit over-rated.

Chapter 1

♡

'What am I doing here?' thought Jewel Lovely, eighteen, with long, tanned coltish legs, long blonde hair falling over her tanned shoulders, eyes of the bluest blue and young, firm, high, firm, tanned breasts. "'I must be crazy.'

Just yesterday she had been ordinary young Jewel Lovely, fresh from finishing school with long blonde hair and young firm breasts, and so on, now here she was in France in the beautiful chateau which belonged to the mysterious Count de Glans, lying on the biggest double bed she had ever seen, stretched out like a cat, drinking chilled champagne and luxuriating in the feel of the expensive silk sheets against her naked skin.

Suddenly there was a knock on the door.

'Who is is it?' she said, hastily wrapping a sumptuous and expensive white silk dressing gown around her lithe and nubile young body with its firm young breasts and really quite spectacular arse.

'It is Louis,' came a husky, masculine voice and she opened the door to see the mysterious Count standing there, naked except for a studded leather codpiece and a tiny yellow bowler hat.

'I just wanted to check that you were settled in alright,' he said huskily. 'Oh, I'm sorry,' he went on, huskily. 'I did not know you had no clothes on.'

Jewel looked into his brooding, deep, blue eyes, set in a chiselled, tanned face with a small scar on the chin. She wanted to dive into those eyes, to fall into his arms and let him hold her, look after her, make passionate love to her, she wanted to lose herself in an ocean of pleasure, just so long as he got rid of that hat.

'Why, but you are beautifiul,' he said broodingly and came into the room, huskily locking the door behind him. Jewel let the gown slide off her tanned shoulders, her lips quivered, she closed her eyes.

'No, I must not!' shouted Louis, his voice strained and husky with suppressed brooding passion, and he roughly pushed her away from him. She fell onto the satin sheets and felt them cool, against her hot burning skin. She shivered.

'I love you,' she said and rose from the bed... Which is a lot like Jesus, isn't it? Because he *rose from the dead*, didn't he? After he had died for all our sins... and, no, please, please read on, there's only a little bit of christianity in this book, honestly, its not five hundred pages of turgid religious diatribe thinly disguised as an erotic classic... And there are nuns! That's right, nuns! Okay, so maybe they're middle-aged women who spend all their time praying and don't exactly get up to anything naughty, but they are nuns nevertheless.. Honestly, it's really interesting, I mean, don't you ever think about your eternal soul and... please, I promise there'll be some sex, well, perhaps not full sex, just kissing and that, oh please, I mean christianity can be FUN! It really can... there's singing, and clapping and guitars sometimes, and lots of   e mornings and other really, really fun things that   people just like us...

No, don't

BLACK TRIANGLE
erotica for couples

Dear~~est~~ Ted,
for a long time now ab...
as long as I can remembe...
well, not ~~almost~~, actually...
I have been wanting t...
to you about things...
I want to talk about...
have never been abl...
express, I always se...
tongue-tied, but w...
I want to s...

Dear ~~Old~~ Ted,
My dear Ted
Dear~~est~~ Ted. &

FORGET the draina...
in the lower field!!
There are things we
MUST talk about, th...
I don't have the n...
to say to you at...
~~to ~~~~s~~~~ never~~ face to fa...
You MUST have not...
I hesitate to say...
but maybe in you...
feel the same w...
in some small
manly way. Te...
is very very ha...
for me to sa...
but Ted. I —
No, I must —
Dear Ted.
~~XXXXXXXXX~~
There. I'v...

MAYHEW

My dear Ted.
forgive me for writing to you
like this, but for a long time there has
been something ... I've been trying to get
off my ~~strong, manly~~ chest but when I meet
you in person all we ever seem to be able to
talk about is the DRAINAGE in the lower
field — which is not what I REALLY want ~~to~~
say. Basically, you see. Ted, what it is...
Ted, you see ON ~~DAMN~~ ~~DAMN~~ ~~DAMN~~
Ted. I am writing this letter to tell you about
things which I can never say directly to your
face. Basically Ted ~~XXXXXXX~~, ~~I have very great~~
                          manly
I have very ~~strong~~ feelings towards you I have strong
manly feelings ~~which only a man I have~~.
Ted.

and they've taken the gollywogs out of Enid Blyton, you're not allowed to sing baa baa black sheep anymore and they're giving all the lottery money to the limp-wristed brigade, I mean, I'm all for equality, but it's gone too far when they get the same as us.

I'll tell you what, this country would be a better place if all the do-gooders were lined up against a wall and shot. I'm the most patriotic man in this country, but I remember when England was English. I remember the proudest day of my life – when I met Maggie Thatcher at Number Ten. She wanted to congratulate me for all the charity work I'd done for the little kiddies; I'm all heart, me. Maggie's a lovely woman, though I haven't got much time for her family. "You know what you want to do, Maggie," I said. "You want to send 'em all back. Eh? You know what I mean." And then I said "I've seen you fishing for compliments and using a wiggly worm for bait. How queer." and everybody laughed.

The other proudest day of my life was when I received my OBE for big-heartedness from her Majesty the Queen, a lovely woman, though I haven't got much time for her family. "You know what you want to do, Your Royal Highness," I said, with a wink. "You want to send 'em all back." Then I hoiked

Here! How queer! He's a funny little chap with his cheeky grin and odd-looking suit! And I'm on the left, ha ha ha. No, seriously, that's me meeting the founding father of National Socialism.

Everyone always loved my act. There'd be tears and hysterics every time, I tell you. They don't get laughs like that these days, more's the pity. These so-called modern comics could learn a thing or two off me. They're just total rubbish, the whole lot of 'em.

up me trouser legs to show bit of ankle, did a little dance and cried, "I don't know what you're looking at. Who do you think you are, Cousin Keith from Putney Heath? Eh! Where's me washboard?" and her Royal Highness laughed fit to bust.

It reminded me of the time when I first met Adolf Hitler in 1936. He was a lovely warm man with a great sense of humour. "You know what you want to do, Adolf," I told him. "You want to send 'em all back." And then I pretended to hide behind a pillar, saying, "Look out, mum, the Spanish are coming. Quick! Bomb 'em!" then I gave him a saucy look and everybody laughed.

Of course I haven't spent my whole life hob-nobbing with the rich and famous, I was very poor when I was a lad, I didn't know what money was until I was sixteen, and when I first started in showbusiness, I had to really struggle. Up until September 1939, I'll be honest with you, I wasn't the most popular comedian in Britain, (though I was very big in Germany) and I found it very hard to get bookings. Whether this had anything to do with the fact that my act at that time consisted of an hour and a half of Nazi polemic, I shall never know, because once Herr Hitler declared war on England, I knew my friendship with the funny little Austrian had to end. He had a lot of good ideas but declaring war on us was not one of them.

The day war broke out I was due on at the London Palladium, I was almost bottom of the bill, but it was to be my big break. Tommy Cockles was the compère that night, a tall, devious man, I never got on with him – he could never smile, not properly, not like me, I'm all heart, me. Eh! Where's me washboard? Ha, ha. Anyway, I knew that night wasn't the night to do my clever synopsis of Mein Kampf.

Up until September 1939, I'll be honest with you, I wasn't the most popular comedian in Britain, though I was very big in Germany

Yours truly with Chester Drawers. I taught him everything there was to learn about comedy, particularly the bits about getting hit with blunt objects

So, there I was, backstage, waiting to go on, without an act. But, as luck would have it, there was a young northern comic on that night, Chester Drawers, down in London for the first time. He was very nervous and needed re-assuring that his gags would work, and little me, ever the big-hearted Arthur, put all thoughts of my own problems aside and told him to try his act out on me, which he did. After he'd finished it was time for me to go on, "I'll let you know," I said, and I hurried out to face the toughest audience in London.

Well, to cut a long story short, I was a triumph, and when I came off, there was Chester waiting in the wings, ashen-faced. "Chester," I said to him, "That material of yours works a treat. It brought the house down. Ta." Well, Chester went on, and they booed him off. I explained to him after, that that was the difference between him and me – I knew how to tell a gag. It often happens when a northern comedian comes south, the humour just doesn't translate. But I'm all heart, me, and I gave Chester plenty of work over the years as my stooge. I'll say something for him, he knows how to take a punch. I got very friendly with Chester and his wife, Katie, a beautiful, but slightly fragile and nervous woman.

They had a lovely family which I enlarged to the tune of at least one child. I'm not proud of that, mind, but Chester was away touring a lot and Katie needed some company. Chester's in a home, now, and he's been there for many years. It saddens me to see what he's reduced to, so I don't ever visit him. Though I do think about him from time to time, particularly when I'm with my present wife (number seven and this time it's for keeps), Lucy, his grand-daughter.

So, anyway, I was on my way up the ladder of success, and all I needed was a catchphrase. I wasn't getting anywhere trying to think of one until, as luck would have it, I was waiting outside Chester's dressing room one night, listening at the door while he went through some new material he wanted to try out when I heard him say "Where's me washboard?" and, quick as a flash,

GO FOR IT!

CP MAX – CHEESY PEAS ISOTONIC SPORTS DRINK

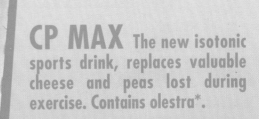

CP MAX The new isotonic sports drink, replaces valuable cheese and peas lost during exercise. Contains olestra*.

CP MAX is a physiologically balanced mix of cheese and peas designed to provide multi-source energy for training.

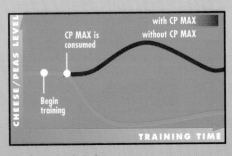

Northern Foods Ltd.

*Note: This product contains olestra. Olestra can cause diarrhoea, loose stools, fecal urgency, nausea, gas and bloating, underwear staining, anal leakage, greasy bowel movements and oil in toilet. Symptoms should go away within 48 hours after you stop eating olestra foods. If symptoms persist consult your doctor.

HOLD THE BELLS!

An indispensable guide to pubs and how to use them by Billy Bleach.

Pubs come in all shapes and sizes. Normally the best boozers are in the worst areas – you don't want to drink somewhere too popular, it's hard to get served, it's difficult to sell nicked gear and chances are some tosser and his muggy family will try and sit next to you.

Here is a list of pubs to steer clear of.

RIVERSIDE PUBS

Give them a swerve. Favourite haunts of the middle-classes. Look out for Volvos in the car park and pesto on the menu. Pesto! Have a word! I thought pesto was someone who got on your nerves in Spain.

REAL ALE PUBS

Nightmare boozers, these, full of beards and men with bunches of keys hanging from their jeans. Most of these blokes are virgins whose idea of a good night out is six pints of Old Scratchfoot followed by a game of Dungeons and Dragons on their own.

Also, real ale pubs never have juke boxes or fruit machines, they give me the creeps just thinking about them.

BIG PUBS

You often get these on the outskirts of town, you can arrange to meet a geezer in one of these and spend the whole night looking for him. You also get a lot of fights in these barn-style boozers and, unless you've got a weapon stashed, chances are you'll get a doing in the car park.

IRISH PUBS

These can be alright, though they can be a bit selective when they serve you if they suss you're not a paddy. You often get some old trout singing along to the juke box after she's had a few (what a racket!). Good for contacts if you're in the building game.

PUBS NEAR POLICE STATIONS

Give them a wide berth for obvious reasons. You can easily spot filth in a pub. Plod will be up at the bar drinking scotch and being loud (uniform). Plainclothes are just as easy, they look like children and never have birds with them.

PUBS NEAR THE DOLE OFFICE

Again – steer clear. Full of grasses and wrong-uns.

RESTAURANT PUBS

Surf and turf, chilli con carne, prawn cocktail, deep-fried potato skins... Bollocks! I go to a boozer for a drink, not to watch some plum from Crawley helping himself to the salad bar.

FAMILY PUBS

I can't even bear to talk about these.

In fact, the only pubs I can whole-heartedly recommend across the board, wherever you are, are...

THE PUBS THAT TIME FORGOT

Brilliant. I love these. They normally have two bars, the lounge and the snug. Always nice and quiet. The snug should be empty apart from one old geezer in a suit drinking light ale. Frosted glass and should still have draught mild. All the sandwiches wrapped in cellophane – ham or cheese, nothing else. People mind their own business in these places, which suits me.

P.S. Should have pickled eggs as well.

PISS OFF, MATE! – PEOPLE TO STEER CLEAR OF IN PUBS

■ People who ask for a read of your paper.
■ People who ask if you want to play darts.
■ People who say "Are you coming to the quiz tonight."
■ People who say "It's no good having real ale if you don't clean the pipes." (Usually bearded.)
■ People who rip open their crisp packets and put them in the middle of the table.
■ People who put Chris Rea on the juke box and then say "I didn't put this on."
■ People with collecting tins. (Unless it's for the little kiddies at Great Ormond Street.)
■ Children. Sling them out unless they're knocking out a bit of gear.
■ Foreigners who ask – "Do you have coffee?"
■ Posh people who sit next to you when you're watching the football on SKY and make out that they're your mate.

The worst type to avoid in any pub is the self-styled "King of the boozer". You know, the type that's always there but doesn't seem to have any mates. He'll tell you how to win on the fruit machine, what to put on the juke box, how to operate the fag machine, how to deal with your girlfriend. I've met so many blokes like this, you wouldn't believe it.

MEDUS
Industries

World leaders in the field of valves and valve pumps since 1974

Chairman's statement

Chairman of Medus Industries plc
Andrew Lester

1996 has been another good year for Medus Industries plc, we have made significant advances in some of the most competitive markets in the world and at the same time greatly improved our financial performance.

With sales at £38 million producing a pre-tax profit of £2 million we are well placed to go into the next century

We fully believe that our valves and valve-based pumps are second to none. Globally we have an installed product base of over 3,250,000 products and a client list that includes blue chip companies in almost every country in the world. We are a leader, not a follower, in international collaboration in commercial, governmental, and military spheres.

Our proven project management skills make us supremely skilled in co-ordinating the implementation of our products into any large-scale project.

We have developed modern, efficient, high technology valves that can compete with the best in the world. And with the unprecedented success of the new Kellet 186 Valve we

Above: Our new high-tech premises on Wallwark Road.
Right: The Kellet 186 marine valve, incorporating a miniature ISEC and the world's first AE523 spec. mini turbine hopper.
Far right: A picture of a monkey.

are now unassailable in the all-important, multi billion dollar arena of the marine suction market.

The revolutionary design of the Kellet valve incorporates a miniature ISEC (integrated switched emission control) made of Kevlar which makes it look like a sort of space ship or something! Or even a space gun!

Our new offices are a lovely blue colour, like a blue racing car

Our long-awaited move to larger premises on Wallwark Road was a real shot in the arm and meant that our planned expansion continues smoothly and efficiently. The facility includes the very latest state-of-the-art concepts in modern office construction and design. We have seized the opportunities provided by the move to implement efficiency improvements, and we will continue to obtain the benefits of this restructuring in the future.

We have recently introduced a performance related pay scheme, initially at a senior level only, in order to align the interests of staff with those of the company. In addition, the remuneration committee is developing a long-term incentive plan for which shareholder approval will be sought in 1997. With a leaner, fitter workforce we are well-poised to meet ever-changing needs into the millennium

Our continuing drive for greater efficiency will keep us competitive in the years ahead

We have continued to pursue strategies designed to extend the international strength of the company. It has been particularly pleasing to see Medus expanding into the United States, traditionally a very tough market to penetrate, and at the beginning of the

year I flew out to our new offices in Miami. Yes, I did! I went to AMERICA! I flew on an aeroplane and everything. And we all went to Disneyworld and I shook hands with Pluto, though I wanted to shake hands with Mickey, but I couldn't. Pluto was all right, though.

Hooray, it's my birthday tomorrow

So the future is looking good. We continue to develop our product range, and to prioritise our customer

interface, which in turn places us in a competitive position to achieve an ever-increasing share of the growing opportunities available in the switched valve/pump valve/industrial suction and pumping market around the world, or something.

Andrew Lester, Chairman
March 6 1997

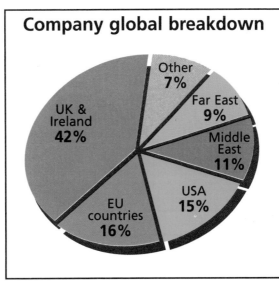

A pie chart showing the relative sizes of our markets. I hope I get the biggest slice of pie, and I hope its cherry! With custard. Hooray!

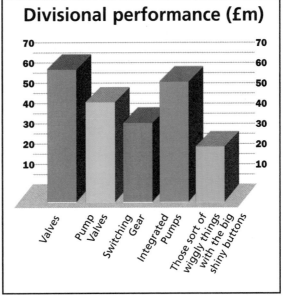

Look, this looks like sort of towers or skyscrapers, or something, doesn't it?

SPOT THE DIFFERENCE

Can you spot twenty differences between these two pictures featuring the lovable cockney rogue, Chris?

JED'S CARPENTRY WORDSEARCH

```
R A R S E A A R S E
A R S E A R S E E S
R S E S R A R S E R
S E A R S E R S R A
E S R A E A R S E R
A R S E A R S E E S
R A E R R S A R S E
A R S E S E R A R S
S E S R A R S E A R
E S R A R S E S R A
```

Our old friend Jed Thomas has hidden twenty words to do with carpentry and woodwork in the grid right, all you have to do is find them. Remember, you can go horizontally, vertically or diagonally in any direction. Find these hidden words:

TENON SAW	CARPENTER	RULER
HAMMER	CABINET	PLIERS
SCREWDRIVER	DOVETAIL	DRESSER
HAND DRILL	MAHOGANY	PLANE
WORK BENCH	FURNITURE	MALLET
SET SQUARE	ARCHITRAVE	WALNUT
PLUMB LINE	CHISEL	DOWEL

WHO'S THERE?

Here's a clever two-part puzzle for you. First colour in the picture, left, using the key below. Then, to find out who it is, complete this simple quiz, fitting each answer into the grid.

KEY:
1: PINK   2: YELLOW
3: BROWN   4: WHITE
5: BLUE   6: RED
7: BLACK   8: ORANGE

CLUES:
1) Complete this saying: "Suit _ _ _ sir"
2) You use it to colour walls: P_ _ _ _
3) Complete this saying: "Little boys should be _ _ _ _ and not heard"
4) Yuppie flu: _ _
5) Opposite of left: _ _ _ _ _

GRIPPED!

T he former Yugoslavia was once a prime Mediterranean destination for British holiday makers, but sadly the forces of nationalism, racism and aggression have made sure that the area is now firmly off the general holidaymaker's map. But what a lot of people don't realise is that, luckily, it is now one of the prime off-roading paradises in the world! With the roads pitted and pot-holed, the bridges blown away, the countryside bombed to bits it might have been designed for four wheel drive fun. If you think you've done it all, think again! With its huge water-filled craters to negotiate, deserted villages to roar through and countless mine-fields to pick your way across, this is one serious FWD challenge.

To prove it, Simon Bush and Lyndsay Mottram, spent three weeks testing the terrain for readers of **Gripped!**

The hat – THE famous hat!!

We set off

Hi, yeah, Simon and Lyndsay, here, with, of course, she who needs no introduction – the Beast! We spent a week loading her up and now we are gripped, sorted and ready to rock.

Showed Lyndsay my new state of the art sleeping bag – made of a special material developed by NASA and able to withstand temperatures of minus 200. I could tell he was impressed, he's only got some awful old army surplus khaki affair which stinks.

Left the safe haven of home at 06.30 with a clarion call to the neighbours of "Let's off road!" Two comrades setting off on the adventure of a lifetime. I must say I'm glad to be in the company of the best mate a guy could ever have. I know that when things get tough I'll feel secure knowing Lyndsay is at my back. The rear axle snapped a hundred yards down the road and we spent the rest of the day fixing it.

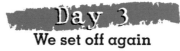
We set off again

A steaming hot jungle of a morning. This time we got off without a hitch and headed for Eurostar and The Chunnel. Long delays to get on the train, sat in the baking hot car park for several hours. Eventually told to drive on only to discover that the tarmac had melted and we were stuck fast. Missed train. Spent night in car park. Zip got stuck on my new sleeping bag, couldn't get it out. Lyndsay refused to share his bag and I spent an uncomfortable night aboard The Beast.

Day 3
We set off again

Freed by some holidaymakers in a Nisssan Micra. Got on train. "Let's off-shore!" we cheered as we plunged into the mighty tunnel. Train got stuck.

Spent uncomfortable night aboard train. I managed to free the zip on the sleeping bag and spent a couple of hours demonstrating all the special features to Lyndsay, who pretended to be asleep.

France

Train finally arrived in La France. Once we'd got the Beast started we hit the tarmac and headed for all points East. Tiring of the mundane world of the metalled blacktop, we soon elected to go off-road across the rugged French countryside. Got stuck.

Lyndsay nor I can pronounce. You know the sort of thing; tents, tin huts and the khazi is a hole in the ground. The local guys have told us they're going to prepare us a traditional Yugo dish, done the authentic way. Look forward to it. Despite being totally cream-crackered after our epic trek we studied the maps. Sorted. Our route will take us on the most testing off-road assault course ever devised by man or beast. It's gripped. As well as gorges, boulders, ravines and all the usual off-road fayre Lyndsay has decided to take us right into the crater of an active volcano. He's mad!!!! Luckily, so am I. Let's off road!

Day 9
The Quest begins

Traditional Yugo meal not a great success, turns out the hole in the ground wasn't the khazi after all, it was some kind of barbecue pit. The real khazi is a well-equipped brick building. Decided to set off first thing before anyone was up. Problemmo-time – The Beast wouldn't start.

Luckily a Croat geezer offered to fix it. Sorted. I think he was impressed with my beard. Dismantled engine. Unsorted.

Days 5–7
Onwards

Too many adventures crossing Europe to recount here, they'll have to wait for another day. Suffice to say, it was mammoth! Sleep became something of a luxury as we hammered through a gob-smacking world of fields, green lanes, ditches, bogs and tractor tow-ropes. We can now say "Excuse me, could you pull us out, please?" in five different languages.

Day 8
Welcome to hell

Arrive at the base camp in Besko something or other, which neither

We had a long chat about what bastards the Serbs were, at least I had a long chat, he was more the strong silent type.

Day 9 (night)
The Quest begins again

Lyndsay, the drongo, had omitted to tell me that we are in fact in Serbia and not Croatia. I can't tell the difference, they're all bloody fascists. Thanks Lyndsay, you're a pal, I don't think. We slipped out under cover of darkness, pushing The Beast. We had no choice in the latter because the engine is still dismantled, since the mechanic went off to get some mates before he'd finished. Luckily we bumped into a UN peace keeping force a short distance down the road. They all looked to be about twelve and appeared to be scared shitless of us. As we tried to explain what had happened they all surrendered and gave us a state of the art Bulgarian jeep. Well-sorted! Radical!

Day 10
The Quest continues

Bulgarian Jeeps will not set the off-road world alight. On close inspection we found the engine to be a 50cc "Honda Dash" moped model and the chassis to be made of balsa wood. This actually proved to be a bonus when we became stuck in a ditch, as a passing peasant was able to lift us out by hand. Swapped Bulgarian 4WD for 4-Legged, all terrain donkey. Lyndsay now thinks he is Clint Eastwood, and is beginning to annoy me, particularly as he has been talking all day in an irritating husky whisper.

Day 11
In Deep

Donkey gone. Lyndsay claimed to have "parked" it last night. He thinks it's funny. I see no redeeming features anymore in the snivelling little creep and can't think why I ever asked him to come. Pissed in his hat while he was asleep.

Day 12
Down, down, deeper on down

Lyndsay gone. Sleeping bag burnt to a crisp. Got bus to nearest town. Bus got stuck. Seriously pissed off.

Days 13–16
The Lost Weekend

Have spent several days drinking heavily in miserable fly-blown bar in the former somewhere or bloody other. Will I never see home again?

Day 17
Reconciliation

Out of the blue, Lyndsay turned up this morning, said he'd been searching all over for me. Claimed he was sorry about what had happened,

and to make up for it, he'd commandeered a new off-road vehicle that he'd found abandoned by the roadside. We shook hands and made up, though drew the line at hugging. Turns out the vehicle is a medium-sized tank. Gripped! The job's a good 'un! I took the controls while Lyndsay navigated. Now, this is what I call an all-terrain vehicle!

Day 18
Homeward Bound

Sparked off a major international incident when we somehow arrived in Northern Italy, ploughed through a couple of small villages and couldn't stop until we hit Rome, quite literally, slight damage to the Coliseum. Ditched tank and headed for the airport. Got out just in time.

GRIPPED!
THE FORMER YUGOSLAVIA

TERRAIN	10
SCENERY	4
ACCOMODATION	4
FUEL COST	10
LYNDSAY'S CRUMPET RATING	0
TOTAL	**28**

THE ADVENTURES OF UNLUCKY ALF

RISPOORT AAN POLIZEI SWANGERSKAB

Staajtion	Djat	Nuimbr
Amsterdam Centraal	14 Jiuun 96	0003172

Naam	Prijnaam	Nat
CLARKE	Roy & Renee	------

Ajdressen
17 Maple Close, Benchill, Wythenshawe, Manchester, England

Dijtaale

My husband Roy and I recently visited your city of Amsterdam hoping for a holiday filled with tulips and windmills re. Van der Valk. In exploring the city we wandered across narrow streets difficult to view due to the gloomy red lighting. The local ladies seemed very friendly waving happily at tourists from their windows.

Roy decided to ask one of the ladies where he could find the dyke that the little boy had put his finger into all those years ago. She seemed to want payment and not being conversant in the currency Roy handed her what we later found to be £40.00 in English money.

She started to lead Roy to a dingy little room. When I began to follow I was asked for further monetry monies to change hands. It was at this point I sought police activity on my behalf.

Roy soon realised the lady had undressed her clothes and that she had little or no interest in his tourist requirement and kept him a good half hour completely wasting his time.

Although my husband Roy does not wish to press charges the experience did leave him bilious. I as a tourist to your once beautiful country feel these women are cashing in on a marvellous traditional fable about a little dutch boy and his heroism involving the dyke.

I would hate less astute visitors to your country to fall for this cruel con and suggest a warning should be placed in all books c̶

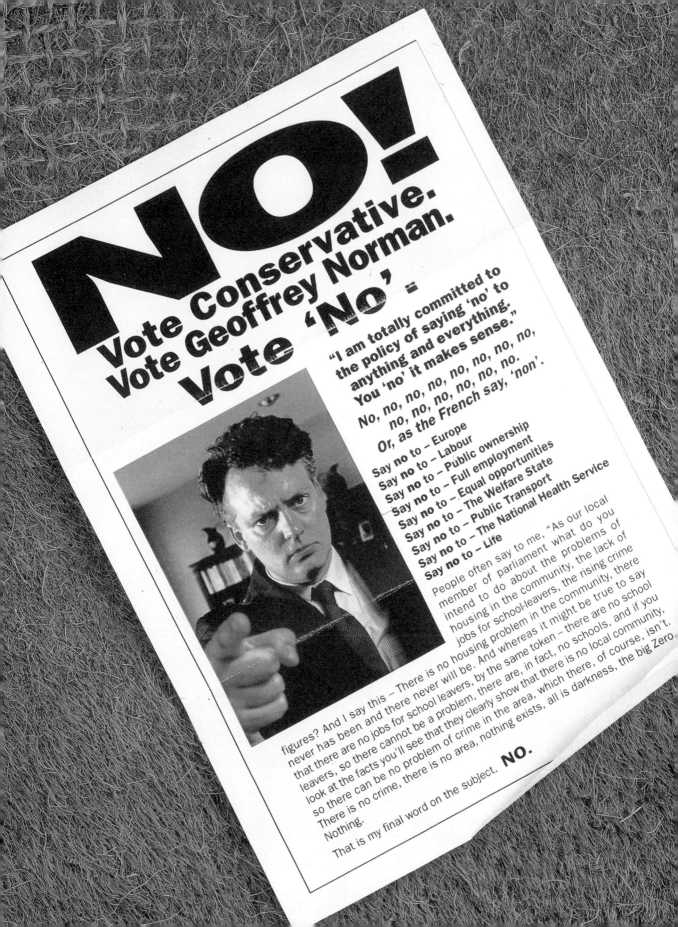

NO!

Vote Conservative.
Vote Geoffrey Norman.
Vote 'No'.

"I am totally committed to the policy of saying 'no' to anything and everything. You 'no' it makes sense."

No, no, no, no, no, no, no, no, no, no, no, no, no, no.

Or, as the French say, 'non'.

Say **no** to – Europe
Say **no** to – Labour
Say **no** to – Public ownership
Say **no** to – Full employment
Say **no** to – Equal opportunities
Say **no** to – The Welfare State
Say **no** to – Public Transport
Say **no** to – The National Health Service
Say **no** to – Life

People often say to me, "As our local member of parliament what do you intend to do about the problems of housing in the community, the lack of jobs for school-leavers, the rising crime problem in the community, there figures? And I say this – There is no housing problem in the community. And whereas it might be true to say that there are no jobs for school leavers, by the same token – there are no school leavers, so there cannot be a problem, there are, in fact, no schools, and if you look at the facts you'll see that they clearly show that there is no local community, There is no problem of crime in the area, which there, of course, isn't. Nothing. so there can be no problem of crime in the area, nothing exists, all is darkness, the big Zero.

That is my final word on the subject. **NO.**

I have been sleeping with my boyfriend for 7 months now. I think I am generally pretty adventurous, and we've been really happy. But now he's asking if he could place a carrot in a place that a carrot was never intended to be placed, and not only carrots, other vegetables as well. I think that this could be quite dangerous and also very painful. I want to hold back but he's pressurising me and says that I'm a prude. What should I do? I really love him but I'm not sure how far I should go.

JANE, NOTTINGHAM

Yes, it's dangerous. Yes, it hurts. Wise up, girl, he just wants to degrade you. Don't do anything you don't want to do. Your body belongs to you and doesn't exist to serve your boyfriend and his sick vegetable-based fantasies. Take control of your life. If this is so important to him then perhaps you need to re-think your whole relationship. In other words get some respect or get rid!

I have been sleeping with my girlfriend for 7 months now. She's generally pretty adventurous, and we've been really happy, but now I'd like to experiment with vegetables a bit. She is reluctant, however and says that it is potentially quite dangerous and also painful. I don't want to pressurise her but find that I am obsessed with the idea of putting a carrot somewhere other than on my dinner plate. What should I do? What are the facts? I really love her, and don't want to hurt her.

JAKE, NOTTINGHAM

Poor ooo-ooo. Some girls just don't know, or even care, what boys like – they don't undrestand that you should do _anyfink!_ to keep your man happy (sorry about my spelling, but my fingers are a bit ikkle for this typeriter, oops! And I'm not vewy good at typing, anyway, it's quite hard actually.) I fink you should chuck your howwid girlfriend, she's probably a lezzie, anyway, if she doesn't like carrots. I hope you don't think I'm too rude and naughty saying this, but I love carrots! In my book it's no-holes barred. Oo find

"Dear Miss Different"

Our Agony Sister sorts out all your problems each month. Write to: Vanity Hair Magazine, Kings Reach Tower, London SE1 9PL

yourself a nice girl who doesn't know much about anyfink, cos then you could teach her everyfink oo like bestest. You deserve that. I fink you sound really swoony and hunky and I would do anyfink to keep a love as true as yours, if you would let me.
Swooon!

My boyfriend has left me after three months and I feel so worthless and miserable. I can't face going out or seeing my friends.

CATHERINE, CHESHIRE

Pull yourself together, you snivelling little doormat. No one is going to respect you if you can't respect yourself. You don't need a man to give you a sense of worth. Get out and enjoy yourself for pity's sake.

My girlfriend has left me after three months and I feel so worthless and miserable. I can't face going out or seeing my friends.

ANGUS, CORNWALL

Oh that's tewwible. Girls can be so howwid sometimes, can't they? I much pwefer boys. That rotten, rotten cow! She dosn't deserve a strong, handsome man like oo. I'm free on Friday – and Saturday. In fact I'll re-arrange my schedule, my whole life, to fit in with oo! Is that better?

I have a problem at work. My boss made a lewd suggestion to me at our last Christmas party which I laughed off, but ever since then he's been making passes at me and commenting on my appearance. I'm sure if I make a fuss he'll sack me. What should I do?

JULIE, OXFORD

Cut his balls off, I mean, you keep a pair of scissors in your desk, don't you?

Honestly, he's the one who should be sacked, not you. Look, I haven't got time for this, I'm a busy professional woman with her life sorted out. Are we still living in the middle ages, or what? Quit whinge-ing and take action, if he sacks you run screaming to the Equal Rights Commission and watch the bastard squirm.

I have a problem at work. I made a light-hearted remark to one of my (female) employees at our last Christmas party and she appeared to take it seriously. She's single, you see, and naturally a bit desperate. Ever since then she seems to take everything I say or do as some kind of a sexual advance. It's all harmless, good-natured stuff like pinching her bottom, pressing up against her at the photocopier and making the odd comment about her breasts (which aren't that fantastic, actually), but she's been really catty with me and she's creating a very bad atmosphere around the office. I'm thinking of getting rid of her, what should I do?

MARK, WOODSTOCK

Well, I weally must say you've been vewy bwave putting up wiv the hysterical old cow for even a minute (she's probably having her menopause, yuk!) I feel weally, weally sowwy for oo. You sound like a very funny man wiv lots of clever and brilliant jokes to play around the office. I wish I could work under a man like you, what fun we could have (oops, that sounded a bit naughty, didn't it?) I'd sack the silly old moo, and replace her with someone younger and blonder and more stupider. P.S. My breasts are really quite lovely, tee hee.

cool sounds

Chip Monk and the Trad Compromise
Lil' Ukelele Larry
You can really imagine yourself dancing through the streets of New Orleans with a giant papièr maché head on. But beware of Coco Mendez' vibraslap which adds a vague whiff of voodoo to this otherwise innocent track. Scary, but nice.
Released February 12 on RCA Records

The Participants
Muthaf∗∗∗er! Whatcha wanna go do a funky thing like that fo' sistuh, y'awl knows this ain't the hood to go shakin' yo booty in!
Great!
Released February 19 on Kill Th' Bitch

The Curly Neighbour Indo-Jazz Adventure
Mutter paneer jive
What can I say? Indo-Jazz. Great. A chance meeting on the streets of Pakistan brought legendary Sixties flugelhorn player Curly Neighbour together with tabla-playing street fakir Dhami Kupa. The result? East meets west with some Indo-Jazz thats hotter than a chilli vindaloo. Phew!
Released February 5 on Jazzharmonic

Butane featuring Clam
Digging Things
Any serious jazz fusion fan will know that Butane have been around for many years now. But now that they have enlisted the aid of veteran session bass-spanker Clam (real name: Clam! Great!) they can't really put a note wrong. With his trusty instrument in hand, there's more slapping going on than in an Alpine dance-fest.
Released February 12 on Obscure Records

Maurice Kwende Trio
Theme from Bullseye
Nigeria's finest rework the popular Yorkshire TV quiz theme as a Jazz/Soca waltz. A little off the beaten track for jazz populists but for those with a taste for jazz adventure Maurice has many other courses to serve up. Give a long listen to his awesome first album 'Listen with Mother'. Wonderful.
Released February 5 on Lagos Music

Stone Windsor's Alchemy 7
Jazz Wand
Stone's no stranger to an avant garde time signature of 17/11 – great! So when you hear the bridge in this particular number, you'll actually belive that Stone's not holding his trademark soprano sax, but a jazz wand. Nice.
Released February 5 on Wrong Note Records

Jack Thimble's Bebop Bone
Talon
The furious pace of this bop favourite reminds me of an XJS sat in the fast lane, showing no mercy to other road users. Reminiscent of the track 'Jack Thimble be nimble' from his first album 'Saveloy'. Here Jack's furious fingers are letting off some serious jazz steam. Niiice.
Released February 19 on A.O.N. Records

Marita Mendoza's Samba Conspiracy
Chip Chap Ayeeee
This up-tempo street samba will have you tapping just about anything you can get your hands on to tap. With the almost budgie-like vocals of Miss Mendoza and the added bonus of Stamford Brook on marimba, this instant Latin jazz classic will have you shouting Chip Chap Ayee for, oh, about a week. Great!
Released February 26 by Satchmo Records

Woody Wilson's Blues Hotchpotch
Howdy Mrs Washerwoman
Mmmm… this'll tempt your jazzbuds as Woody – Mr Wilson to me, great! – whips up an inferno, as the only living exponent of jazz barrel organ.
Released February 26 on Arsoolie

Jazz is this summer's coolest groove. Hot, cool, latin or acid, there's a jazz style out there to suit all tastes. We asked Louis Balfour from TV's *Jazz Club* to reveal the best of this month's new releases.

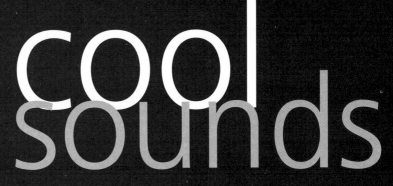

COMING SOON FROM
ERAS Video

Don't miss these exciting new releases from Eras video, available to rent from your local video shop now!

Where It's At

The lives of the pupils at a tough inner city high school are transformed by the arrival of an inspirational new geography teacher who turns them on to geography by conducting lessons in rap. Soundtrack includes Ice T, The Frightening Gangstas and Lonnie Donnegan.

Sensuous Secrets II*

Another erotic masterpiece from Ziggy Krapmeister. Beautiful and innocent Tweed Bountiful tries to discover the whereabouts of her missing sister (Paisley Bountiful from Sensuous Secrets I) and is soon drawn into a world of dark and sensuous desires. Beautiful locations, an intriguing plot, but more importantly, sex in a lift, sex in a swimming pool, masturbation scene, seduction by glamorous older woman, plus group sex with strangers wearing masks. And coming soon...

Sensuous Secrets III in which

youngest sister, Tafetta Bountiful, goes in search of her missing sisters and is drawn into a world of etc. etc. blah, blah, blah...

Babs Wire

An all action thriller starring Barbara Windsor.

*please note the attractive woman in skimpy underwear on the front of the video box does not appear in the film.

103 Dalmatians*
Not 101! Not 102! But 103!
Yes, 103 dalmatians! Just count 'em!

Heroin Galore
A remake of the ever-popular Ealing classic, Whisky Galore, from the makers of Shallow Grave and Trainspotting. When a shipment of grade A heroin is washed up on the shores of a remote Scottish island, the colourful local residents don't know what's hit them! In hilarious scene after hilarious scene they use it on their corn flakes, in their tea, on their chips, to make cakes with, to clean their teeth with, to feed their children with, and then they die.

Babe II – Market Day
A sequel to the popular children's movie featuring a pack of talking sausages.

My Aching Heart
A first for Hollywood, in which a real person, not an animal or an animated character, talks intelligently.

To The Devil A Dieter
Work-out video with a satanic theme.

The Porno Nuns
An early effort from noted Polish director Karel Tetsnarz. This is the moving story of a strict religious community struggling against the odds in the small Lithuanian village of Porno.

Shove it, Grandma
Early British comedy starring Arthur Atkinson. Eras is proud to present a new 'colour' version of this oft-overlooked gem (available in Red or Yellow).

*Several animals were hurt in the making of this film.

That's Amazing!

Another look at the world of the strange and the bizarre with Carl Hooper

"Hello, there! Wasn't it William Shakespeare who said 'There are more things in the world than you could ever dream of, mate?' Well, how right he was. Here are just a few of the amazing facts and figures I've collected over the years. So, join me now, as I lift the lid on the uncanny and delve deep into the dustbin of the inexplicable."

The Jupiter Stone

▼ USE THESE GLASSES TO VIEW THE JUPITER STONE ▼

Here is an actual shard of the famous Jupiter Stone. As you can see, it's completely invisible! The only known truly invisible substance in the world, it can only be seen through these special ultra-high-wave optical glasses, which straighten out the curving waves of light which make the shard appear to not appear, if you see what I mean.

If your copy of the book arrives without the glasses, please, for God's sake, don't write to me, I had sackloads of mail from my last book about the CD of actual space alien speech which for some reason never showed up.

New life discovered in Cairns toilet

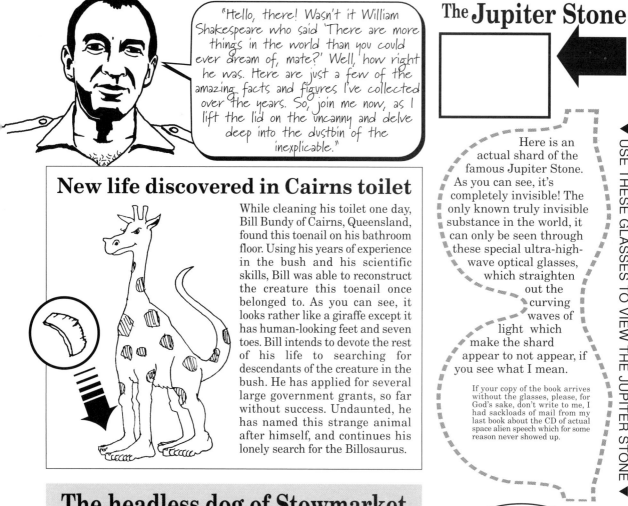

While cleaning his toilet one day, Bill Bundy of Cairns, Queensland, found this toenail on his bathroom floor. Using his years of experience in the bush and his scientific skills, Bill was able to reconstruct the creature this toenail once belonged to. As you can see, it looks rather like a giraffe except it has human-looking feet and seven toes. Bill intends to devote the rest of his life to searching for descendants of the creature in the bush. He has applied for several large government grants, so far without success. Undaunted, he has named this strange animal after himself, and continues his lonely search for the Billosaurus.

The headless dog of Stowmarket

Who would have thought that the sleepy English village of Stowmarket would house one of the unexplained wonders of the animal kingdom? Stuffed and mounted behind glass in the local museum is a dog without a head! Known as the 'Headless dog of Stowmarket'. Some locals claim it is a witch's familiar, others that it is a space alien dog from another galaxy, but if you ask me it's just a dog without a head.

Piece of the sun

Here is an actual piece of the sun, brought back by the Magellan IV probe. Even though it is just a tiny speck it's still incredibly hot. So don't touch it with your bare hands. I dropped the bloody thing six times trying to get it on the page.

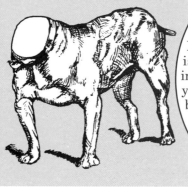

The Stench Spirit

Bya-gwai-onkooroo-gwai-bya-bya-oboorah is the official name of an aboriginal spirit God, but the guys usually just call him by his popular name, Old Stinky. Legends tell how he was Born out of the arsehole of Djanggawulla, the father of all the Gods. You can smell him from a thousand miles away, and the wafting of his stench on the breeze is said to prophesy the coming of a Ngariki-Rongo, or mini cab. This figure is the pictorial representation of Old Stinky, and his magic is so strong that even his picture is said to smell if rubbed.

So, go on, scratch it and get the authentic whiff of Old Stinky. Isn't that amazing?

Optical Illusion

Here's an incredible optical illusion sent to us by Glenn Melton of Canberra. Hold the page up and place your nose on the **X**. Focus your left eye on the figure of the chicken and focus your right eye on the figure of the house. Keeping each eye fixed on the two figures, slowly rotate the page anti-clockwise. After half an hour of this you will see through a portal into the lost city of Atlantis, apparently. Either that, or you'll get a bloody migraine. Guess which happened to me.

X

Dinosaur Sweat

This smear is actual dinosaur sweat – incredible, isn't it! Or should I say, "That's Amazing"? Yes, the sweat of an Apatosaurus, sent in by Mel Tavary of Adelaide. I didn't know that dinosaurs, indeed any reptiles, sweated, but for the purposes of this page apparently they do. Personally I don't care any more.

The Mysterious Document of Brisbane

Probably the most amazing and unexplained thing you will ever see. My bloody contract for 200 more episodes of *That's Amazing*, signed on my behalf by my agent – or should I say my ex-bloody agent.

So there you have it, more bulletins from the world of the strange. More bollocks from the world of the strange, if you ask me. To tell you the truth, I've lost interest in just about everything.

SUIT YOU, SIR!

Were you out with a lady last night, sir?

Was it a lady though, sir?

Does she look over her shoulder at you sir, and make this sort of noise, sir... "ah"?

Now you, too, can boost your confidence with these handy cut-out-and-keep 'Ken and Kenneth' masks. Suitable for any line of work in which you have to deal with the public face to face – including:
★ **Tailors** ★ **Hairdressers** ★
★ **Dentists** ★ **Taxi Drivers** ★
★ **Waiters** ★ **Barmen** ★
And Thousands More!

Ever tried rodeo sex, sir? Call her by her sister's name and see how long you can hang on?

Oooh!

I bet you're hung like a horse, aren't you, sir?

Instructions
1 Cut out a mask along the dotted line, and punch out the holes in each ear.
2 Attach a piece of string or elastic to the ear holes, of a suitable length to fit around your head.
3 Put on the mask and talk to people in an embarrassingly personal and over-familiar manner. Useful phrases to try are dotted around the masks.

Do you ever do the other thing, madam?

Did she want it, sir, did she?

How long do you give it before you turn over, sir?

Do you have a Prince Albert, sir, right through the head? Ooh!

Oooh!

Do you like a vivacious partner, sir, or one that doesn't care what you do as long as she can read Marie Claire afterwards?

Did she succumb, sir, or did you woo her with a battery powered instrument?

Do you like the continental madam, or the full English?

Pleasure's very close to pain, don't you think madam?

BCM BROKERS EMPLOYEE ASSESSMENT PROGRAMME STAGE 1.

Work on the dealing floor of a large international brokers obviously requires advanced decision-making skills, the ability to work fast under pressure, take the initiative when necessary and keep a cool, clear head at all times. Please take a few moments of your time to complete this simple questionnaire, so that we can create a complete personality profile of you.

    Circle either yes or no. Work quickly. The whole test should take no more than fifteen minutes. If you are unsure of your answer, leave the question and come back to it. There is space below each question to make notes or give information in support of your answer. These will not be taken into account when your test is assessed.

Name: ~~DAVE~~ ~~David~~ D. Dave Can I come back to this one?

1. Are you decisive?... ~~YES~~ NO?

Are you joking? I am "Mister Decisive". When I make my mind up about something that's it. Solid. You ask any of my mates. Although, that's not to say that I jump in without thinking about things, no, no, no. No. And, I mean, I have changed my mind about things before now, obviously, so, er, I think that's everything covered isn't it? Lets move on... Or should I just clarify the above? No, I'll move on.

2. Do you enjoy practical jokes? .... YES ~~NO~~ No.

I remember that time someone deliberately left a load of ice cubes lying on the floor of the pub on purpose. That was bloody stupid. Someone could have slipped on them and really hurt themselves. Oh yeah, it's all a big joke until someone gets hurt. Ken, the landlord's, gone past with a tray full of Guinness and he's gone arse over tit. We've pissed ourselves laughing for about ten minutes. It was fantastic, totally creased us up. So, no, I don't like them. Do I? Sorry, this might not be very clear, it's just I'm still not sure if I've answered that decisive question above properly. What do you think?

3. Have you ever cried during a film?....................... yes. ~~YES~~ (NO) No

Have they sent me the wrong form? Me? Blub? Mind you, that one about the pig, that was a bit sad, well it was tragic I blubbed like a kid and I'm not ashamed. Yeah, I well up easy, I'm a pretty emotional bloke, really. But, you know, not that emotional. I mean, I'd never cry at a bloody film or anything like that. Blokes bawling is embarrassing. Mind you, I've cried buckets at football before now, and that bit in Bambi where his mum gets shot... I mean blimey... sorry.....

4. Do you enjoy a quiet hour or two of thought each day? . . . . YES NO YES?

Hmmm. Not sure what they're driving at. Come back to this one. Although maybe not. I suppose I should though....if I've got time. Oh, oh, now I've got meself a bit confused...

6. Would you like to be a famous celebrity? . . . . YES—? NO ?

What a nightmare. Tabloids digging the dirt on your past, no privacy, photographers following you about, all those birds, dosh, free tickets for the cup final and that, arseing about all day, and having a laugh down some club all night, fantastic! I mean, awful. Have I got this right? Only I can't tell anymore. This is beginning to get to me a bit, you know.

7. Do you feel you worry too much? . . . . .hang on YES no NO

Nah. Life's too short isn't it? I always say if you worry you die, and if you don't worry you die. Oh, my God, I'm going to die. Not now, but one day I'm going to die. Just think of that for a minute and let that sink in. I mean, Jesus Christ. Mind you, I believe in, you know, sort of God and an afterlife and that, so, I tend not to worry about mortal things like a non-believer might. If it's all true, that is. I mean no one can be sure for certain can they? Can they? Aaah.

ignore this one
8. Do you believe there is life elsewhere in the universe? . . . . YES NO
nope.

No, there can't be. We'd have found it by now, surely. It's just some kind of cosmic accident that life exists on earth, isn't it? (I put it a bit more clearly in the answer above) I mean, the universe is expanding at the speed of light, my mate reckons, mind you he does talk a lot of bollocks. Though I do agree with him on this one. You know if it's that big, there's got to be some form of life out there, statistically and that. And what about them UFOs and all that. What's that, if not some big cover-up? Although, personally I don't go along with all these conspiracy theories. So, no, or do I mean the other one, you know, the opposite to no, oh God, I don't know.

WE'RE ALL GOING TO DIE! Aaahhagh. MUM!

Medical Matters

Our monthly medical advice column with Doctor Sidney Fraude

I am 49 years old and have recently been promoted, so that I am now working very long hours, but, even though I am very tired all the time, I suffer from very bad sleepless nights. I am also short of breath a lot of the time, I sweat a lot, and I frequently experience a racing heart and feelings of panic. I often have pains in my stomach coupled with diarrhoea and I also have whitish spots on the underside of my tongue which are quite painful.

There's no two ways about it, it is stress. Pure and simple. That's why you've got that upset tummy. What you need is plenty of rest. Go to bed early, with a nice hot cup of cocoa and a good book...

Nothing too exciting, mind. And try not to worry about things so much. As for the spots on your tongue, I could not possibly diagnose them by post, as it were. I wouldn't want to tell you it was something hideous and life threatening, only for you to find out that it wasn't. Or vice versa... I mean, what if I said there's nothing wrong with you and then you died a hideous lingering death exploding from every orifice... I mean, it wouldn't bother me, particularly, but you wouldn't be very happy, would you? So, as I say, you should see a specialist as soon as is humanly possible.

So, there you are, then. Just try to relax with a nice hot cup of cocoa and a good book. Stress will kill you quicker than anything. By the way, there is something hideously wrong with you, but I'm not even remotely qualified to tell you what it is.

P.S. If you feel a panic attack coming on, go with it, it might be a laugh.

My ten year old son has had all the usual jabs, but now they are saying he needs to have more. There has been a lot of conflicting evidence in the news about vaccinations lately. What are the facts? What exactly is this new vaccination for? Where do they get the vaccines from? Are there any harmful side effects? I am very confused about all this.

Come on, where's your sense of adventure? Why not take a trip into the unknown with medical science? What exactly this new vaccination is for, I haven't got a clue, but I get a tenner for every one I do, so I'm all for it. Let's just say it'll prevent ... everything. Every disease known to mankind. So, where does the vaccine come from? Out of an old dead monkey, I should think. As for harmful side effects. Well his teeth could fall out, his eyes could roll back into his head, his temperature could become wildly unstable and his entire immune system could be totally destroyed, but who's to say all of those things might not happen anyway? With a bit of luck nothing will start to show for about twenty years by which time I'll be retired. So get on with it! Get him jabbed, the new vaccine'll be out of date in a minute.

p.s. I'm not even remotely qualified to be doing this job, you know? Complete fraud.

Could you explain to me how homeopathy works? I am interested in alternative approaches to curing eczema, as traditional Western medicine doesn't seem able to help me treat my condition.

Bugger me! I've been hoping that somebody was going to ask me about this. It just so happens that I have recently started to practice homeopathy as a lucrative side-line to the usual willy-nilly prescription of dangerous drugs. Most doctors pooh-pooh alternative medicine, but I say, if there's money in it, it should be thoroughly investigated. The way homeopathy works is (and this is like a dream come true) I give you minute doses of poison, and you get used to it, or something. I'm making this up really, but as you don't even need to be remotely qualified to practice alternative medicine, who cares? Then you can fight off any disease... apparently. Does that sound right? In short, then, I simply poison you... You see? And it's perfectly legal apparently. So why not visit me at the Doctor Fraude Private Institute Of Holistic Medicine, Acupuncture, Crystals, Colonic Irrigation and Voodoo?

Thank you so much to all those readers who took the time to enter our annual Short Story competition. It was difficult to decide a winner as the general quality was very high, and we had literally hundreds of entries. In the end the judges decided to award the prize to Alph R. Mayhew for this beautiful story. Many congratulations Alph, and a £50 Littlewoods voucher is on its way to you.

Handsome young Lord Rafe looked out across the land, his land, land bequeathed to him by his father, and his father before him, and felt heavy with a sense of duty. He looked down and was instantly heartened by the beautiful shine on his immaculate shoes, not an ostentatious brogue, but, er anyway, sorry.

A vague snatch of a song came to him, something about steamy windows, and he hummed tunelessly to himself as he strode manfully, not manfully in a boorish overbearing way, you understand, but in a gentle sensitive sort of manful way, the sort of manliness you might find in Michelangelo's statue of David, that's the sort of manful way he strode across the rutted ground towards the lower field. His lower field, bequeathed to him by his father, and his father before him, er, sorry.

His heart fluttered and skipped a beat and jumped into his mouth and thumped like a big bass drum and sang and felt like breaking as he saw her standing there, mending a fence – Edwina, the beautiful Irish colleen who worked on his land.

Edwina with her mane of flame-red hair, her deep brown eyes and her strong hands and distinctive cap, Edwina, who filled his every waking thought and danced

A many splendoured thing

She filled his dreams – but he was tongue-tied in her presence

merrily through his dreams. Oh Edwina, Edwina, Edwina, or Ed for short.

What would he say to her? What on earth *could* he say to her? Whenever he was in her presence, he found himself tongue-tied and foolish.

'Good morning, Edwina,' he said.

'Good morning sir,' she replied with averted eyes. Always 'Sir', why could she never call him by his name? Were they doomed to forever remain as master and servant? Or could they one day walk arm in arm down the aisle as er... You know, as it were.

'Edwina, I...'

'Two of the sheep got out, sir,' she said, quick as a flash, 'And I need to see to the drainage in the lower field.'

'Yes... Very good... Edwina, I...'

But before he could say anything else, he heard another voice call her name and he looked round to see her father, old Tod, with his mane of grey hair, his deep brown eyes and his strong, manly arms. Tod, whose tireless efforts made sure that the grounds were always in excellent condition. Tod, without whom, Rafe would be lost. Tod who had... How had the poet put it?

Shaped the land with his green hands
Nurtured it with ceaseless toil
Planted, dug with bended back
Breathed his life into the very soil
Made the tender sapling strong
Made the hard earth yield
Dealt with any problem as it came along
Such as the drainage in the lower field...

'Rafe, would you like me to...'

'Whatever you think's best, Edwina,' said Rafe dismissively as he strode manfully over to where Tod stood, like a mighty oak, truly a man among men. The father he'd never had, the brother he'd never had, the friend he'd never had, the er.... no, sorry. No, er forget about Ted, I mean Tod, he

Were they doomed to forever remain as master and servant?

wasn't there. It was Edwina he'd come to see – Edwina, who was a girl in every way, and Rafe, who, of course, was a man in every way. 'Oh, Rafe,' she murmured as she held him in her powerful farm-labourer's arms, and lifted his head up to hers, stroking his

(continued p. 97)

My sex, drink and drugs heaven by Ed Winchester

American news star Ed Winchester, familiar to tv viewers worldwide, has confessed to U.S. fashion magazine *Vanity Hair* that he spent much of his career addicted to drugs and alcohol. "At its height," says handsome Ed (42) "I was on three bottles of vodka a day, mixed with literally tons of coke (cocaine) and speed (amphetamine sulphate). I would party all night and invariably end up in bed with one or more young women having soulless casual sex. It was absolutely f*ck*ng fantastic.

Big

"I thought I was big, I thought I was clever, but what I couldn't foresee was that everyone else would as well. Girls would say 'Ed, you're big and clever, can I s*ck your d*ck?' (suck your dick). It sounds crazy now, but I would just say, 'Yeah, okay.'"

Huge

One day, however, Ed realised that the drinks and drugs were beginning to affect his work, "I was funnier, more popular and was making huge amounts of money. To this day I still don't know why I gave it all up."

St*ff

Since then Ed has cleaned up his act. He has stopped the endless round of partying and pill-popping. He has given up pleasure and chosen life, or, rather, something similar to life but a bit duller. He now appears healthy and fresh-faced, he has quit drugs and drinks only mineral water. When asked how he feels now, he replied "bored st*ff" (shitless).

MYSTIC

Forget the hype. We take an unbiased look forward to the World Cup in 1998. Setting aside jingoistic prejudice, what, seriously, are the chances of the various teams involved?

We asked Ron Manager to take a long hard look into his crystal ball and give us his expert opinion on who he thinks will give us a thrill in France.

Cruciate

World cup? France '98? The stuff of dreams, isn't it? You know, marvellous.

The whole world taking part, football's big party, early exit for brave Scotland, it's my party and I'll cry if I want to. You'd cry too if it happened to you, hmm? Cruciate ligament wrenched, bones torn from the socket, out for the duration, bye bye Gascoigne, isn't it? Marvellous.

Small boys

The Egyptian team, isn't it, looking strong this time, yashmaks for goalposts, ouch mummy,

CON DOC IN DOCK

Evil 'Doctor' Sidney Fraude is in court today to face charges of impersonating a doctor and actual bodily harm. Fraude, who has no medical training at all, worked for twenty years as a GP in Cardiff. He used forged documents to trick his way into the practice and was not even remotely qualified to be doing what he was doing. His list of bizarre treatments included
● PRESCRIBING dog shampoo to an elderly woman with a serious stomach complaint
● ORDERING one patient to take three mothballs with water every day after meals to prevent hair loss
● BREAKING a chair over man's head as part of a so-called physiotherapy session
● KICKING another man in the b*ll*cks "for a laugh"
● TELLING one attractive young female patient with a sprained ankle to remove all her clothes and then taking seven hours to paint a picture of her, which he later exhibited in his waiting room.

'Doctor' Fraude said in his defence, "Lighten up, I was only having a laugh."

RON TALKS BALLS!

The silver-haired senior statesman of soccer gets his crystal ball out

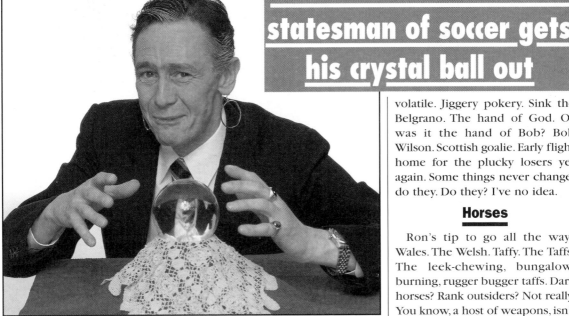

I've trodden on a scorpion. Can you kiss it better? Rubbing the ball in camel dung for your friend to head it. What a smell! It sphinx! Walk like an Egyptian? Why not.

Leather

The Germans as ever in with a chance. Efficient, clinical, well organised, strong, ruthless, leather-clad, blond, jackbooted, ow, ow, whip me again Hans. Make me beg for it. Enduring image, isn't it? You know, the Hitler Youth in the Reichvolkstadionpark. Lugers for goalposts, an easy first round triumph over the Poles. Lebensraum? Don't bet against it.

Gagging

Hooray for Brazil. Bare-footed. Playing on the beach. Marvellous support. Carnival, spectacular outfits, you know, gagging for it. Ronnie Biggs, great train robber, ouch mummy, he's coshed me, isn't it? What a rogue, a wag, he sold his arsehole for punk apparently. Funny old world. Pele, of course.

Slipping

Let's not forget the Japanese. Inscrutable, isn't it. Squad weakened by injury and hari kiri. Defeat unthinkable. Mass suicide on the terraces. Samurai swords twisting and tearing. Banzai! Intestines and blood all over the pitch, players slipping and sliding. Enduring image, isn't it? Players go into hiding, refuse to acknowledge the final whistle, emerging years later. A long way to go before they can match continental sophistication, perhaps, hmmm?

Pokery

Argentina? Hot Latin blood coursing around those veins. Bags of cocaine for goalposts. Chop me one out, mummy. That's better. Tricks and wiles. Passionate, volatile. Jiggery pokery. Sink the Belgrano. The hand of God. Or was it the hand of Bob? Bob Wilson. Scottish goalie. Early flight home for the plucky losers yet again. Some things never change, do they. Do they? I've no idea.

Horses

Ron's tip to go all the way? Wales. The Welsh. Taffy. The Taffs. The leek-chewing, bungalow-burning, rugger bugger taffs. Dark horses? Rank outsiders? Not really. You know, a host of weapons, isn't it. Giggsy? Giggsy Wiggsy? My feet keep dancing, I love to love but Giggsy just wants to dance? Three in a bed? Marvellous. Is Wales the new Brazil? Or is Brazil the old Wales? Hard to tell. Vinny Jones? Come off it boyo.

Langochynmerffingogochstyn? Marvellous.

Chris

This is to Certify That

CHRIS JACKSON
(aka. Chris the crafty Cockney)

Will nick anything.

~

He is a little bit wooor,
A little bit waayyy,
A little bit tasty,
A geezer,
You know, a little bit 'back off'.
He is a One-man Crime wave.

.... INSPECTOR DRISCOLL, METROPOLITAN POLICE

Chris and one
of his mates

REPORT D'INCIDENT OFFICIEL POLICIER

Prefecture	Date	Nombre
Paris XXIIIeme	24 Aout 96	0014257

Nom	Prénom	Né
CLARKE	Roy & Renee	------

Addresse
17 Maple Close, Benchill, Wythenshawe, Manchester, England

Espèces

Myself and Roy (my l'amore) were partaking of a walk down the Champs elise street when we stopped to capture the scene by way of a picture from Roy's Kodac (Birthday present from his sister, now sadly departed).

We noticed a stranger (un homme) regarding us with interest and heavily gesticulating in French that he would take a picture of myself and Roy, although obviously he did not know our names at the time.

I gave him (le homme) the camera and told him to make sure he didn't put his thumb over the lens like Roy's brother Ian did when he tried to take a photograph of myself and Roy at our 20th, and I ended up calling him all sorts of names. At which point I turned to Roy and I said "What did I call him, Roy?" and Roy replied, "all sorts of names". Following this, the stranger took the camera and motioned us to move in a backwards motion in order to get both myself and Roy and the Eiffle Tower (Tower d'Eiffle) all in focus.

Roy pointed out that the stranger had gone a long way back and had actually preceded to mount his moped with the camera in question over his shoulder. The next thing, he began to sped off in the direction of Notre Damm, which we'd visited the day before and found it a little gaudy.

Roy commented quite rightly that we hadn't come on holiday to have our camera stolen. What use are those photo's to him (le homme). They also have 8 pictures of Roy's bowling final in which he came third behind Terry Jackson and Peter Wallis.

Roy did manage to keep hold of the lens cap cover. If this helps track down the criminal we would be glad to donate this to the enquiry of the case.

Not only has the loss of the camera affected our holiday (no photo's to remind us of the pleasant time before the disaster so cruelly befell us in the shape of camera theft) but Roy had three bouts of indigestion due to this incident.

We are hoping the matter can be resolved without us having to contact the British Emmbassy causing a diplomatic incident and bringing Anglo-French relationships to a halt and possibly closing down that tunnel thing.

JESSE'S DIETS

An exclusive behind-the-scenes look at the creation of a TV legend

Jesse's Diets are a popular part of *The Fast Show*. Everyone seems to enjoy Jesse's madcap appearances, but what a lot of people don't realise is the amount of hard work and technical wizardry that goes into creating such apparently simple pieces of film.

A team of writers work round the clock for a year writing the hilarious scripts, and they allow their imaginations to run riot. On paper anything is possible, but it's then the problem of the production team to make those sketches a reality.

"It's a real headache sometimes," says co-producer Paul Whitehouse. "They'll write the first thing that comes into their head, and then we've got to figure out how on earth we're going to film it!"

Construction begins

Work on the mammoth set begins some three weeks before filming is due to start as an army of designers, set construction workers and special effects experts start to construct Jesse's unique world.

Fig 12.1 Is it Mark – or his double, Buster Cash?

The shed that we see Jesse stand in front of is built entirely in the studio – copied exactly, nail for nail, from a real shed that stands in a field in Northumberland. It is this real shed that we see at the start of each sketch filmed from a helicopter.

In this shot the helicopter pilot had the difficult and dangerous task of hovering just above the ground to make it look like the camera was on a standard tripod. Director Sid Roberson insisted on filming the actual sketches in the controlled conditions of the massive Studio One at Pinewood studios – the largest sound stage in the world.

"It would be just too risky filming these elaborate set-ups on location," the muscular director told us.

Once everything is built, it is tested over and over again, so that there is no element of risk, and no chance of any danger to the actors on the day.

Secret cast members

Yes, actors *plural*. In the finished sketches it will, of course, appear to be only one actor playing the entire scene – TV funnyman Mark Williams – but in reality three separate actors are required to make it work. As well as Mark there is his double, Buster Cash and also veteran stunt man Mike Joplin.

This is because, apart from the obvious dangers of filming such an action-packed scene, it is in fact shot on two separate stages. One a special effects stage with a blue screen where Mark performs, and the other the shed set where Mike and Buster perform.

As the door opens it is Buster who comes out, then it is Mark himself who delivers the line, from the safety of the blue screen stage, then it is stunt man Mike Joplin who actually does the difficult and dangerous return through the door. In the final version of the scene, thanks to the very latest computer technology, you won't be able to tell where one actor ends and another begins. It looks simple, but it is the result of nearly eight months of round the clock activity from the technicians at Film-Magic in California pasting the various elements together.

An early start

On the day of shooting Mark is in make up at four am ready for the painstaking five hour make up job that will transform him from a handsome actor into the extraordinary being that is Jesse. And not just Mark! Mike and Buster, too, must undergo a similar ordeal, as it is vital that they all look as nearly identical as possible. The job is

Fig 12.2 *Construction begins at Pinewood's Studio One*

a tough one for Jane Walker and her team of make-up artists, but after five hours Mark appears, unrecognisable, as Jesse, and filming can begin.

Blue screen blues

Mark will spend the day on the special effects stage, standing in front of a blue screen, he must imagine the set and everything that is going on around him, as state of the art computerised cameras record his every facial flicker. These camera moves will be exactly duplicated on the shed set with Buster and Mike standing in for Mark, so that when the two pieces of of film are put together it will appear as if Mark really is standing in front of the shed.

"People think that acting must be very glamourous and exciting," says Mark, eating his lunch through a straw. "But standing up there all day under the hot lights, where your every move is mapped out to the nearest millimetre it can get very boring and tiring. Sometimes the only thing that keeps you going is the knowledge that when it's all put together it'll really blow your socks off!"

Sure enough Mark has to stand on the blue screen stage all day, repeating the same actions over and over, so that all the elements will properly fit together when they marry them in the edit. It's hard work, but Mark keeps everyone amused with a string of hilarious theatrical anecdotes.

Special effects

At six o'clock the exhausted actors get a break and it's the turn of Steve Brubank and his team of special effects geniuses to take centre stage – literally, as they rig the set for the big effects sequence. Behind the scenes it's a tangle of

Fig 12.3 *Director Sid Roberson oversees the action*

wires and switches and explosive devices, and out of shot seven men with remote control handsets wait to manipulate the various objects. Steve himself, trade mark cigar gripped firmly between his teeth, stands behind the space-age computer console which masterminds the whole sequence. Steve is nervous, he knows that if anything goes wrong it's another time-consuming re-rig, and time is money. But nobody else is worried, Steve is the best in the business.

The cameras turn. Steve counts down and the whole set goes crazy. The door opens, a tyre falls to the ground, a piece of litter floats by, and then, as suddenly as it begun, it's all over.

"Cut!"

A round of applause. Once the sound effects are added and the actors are painted into the scene it will be one of the most exciting sequences on *The Fast Show*.

Hair-raising stunts

It's eleven o'clock at night, and the only shot left to do is Mike's big stunt. There is a mood of hushed expectancy on the set. Even Mark has stayed behind to watch, knowing that Mike is only taking these risks to make Mark look good. Mike focuses all his attention on what he has to do. The stunt has been planned and re-planned, there have been countless dry runs, but it's vital that nothing goes wrong when the cameras are rolling. One tiny mistake could cause a disaster. At last Mike is ready, he takes his place on the set, only inches in front of the special door. Stunt arranger Bob Devlin makes his final checks – he signals to Sid, "Okay!"

"Silence on the set! ... And ... Action!"

Mike turns, grips the door handle, lifts the latch, the door

Fig 12.5 Digital wizardry completely disguises Mike Joplin as he performs the most dangerous scene – 'the closing'

Fig 12.4 After a successful day's work, the crew gather to cheer off the undisputed star of Jesse's Diets, TV funnyman Mark Williams

swings open, and as everyone holds their breath he steps back through it into the darkness. The door closes. There's an agonizing wait, then, thumbs up. He's okay! The stunt has gone without a hitch. A cheer goes up from the crew. He's safe. The cameraman checks the gate – "Clean gate! It's a wrap!"

Just the beginning

As the champagne flows, everyone tries to forget that tomorrow they have to do it all again. They've only shot the first sketch, there are another ten to go. And that means another ten long days on the set, not to mention the months of editing, computer effects work and dubbing, when music and sound effects will be added. But right now there's a carnival atmosphere on the set as everyone pats Mike on the back.

All this skilled work and technology doesn't come cheap, however. Says co-producer Charlie Higson, "When you add it all up, the cost of these scenes is somewhere in the region of five million pounds, but I think it's all worth it when you see the finished result on your screens."

To which we can only say, "Hear hear!"

MONDAY 17 OCT 1996   THE FAST SHOW

                                                                CALLSHEET 34

PRODUCERS: CHARLIE HIGSON
            PAUL WHITEHOUSE   SUNRISE: 05:45   MAIN UNIT: 08:00
DIRECTOR: SID ROBERSON   SUNSET: 19:30   COSTUME: 08:30
                                                       MAKE UP: 15:15
UNIT LOCATION: SOUND STAGE ONE, PINEWOOD

ARTIST	CHARACTER	PICKUP	MAKE/UPM/D		ON SET
MARK WILLIAMS	JESSE				
BUSTER CASH	JESSE (DOUBLE)	04:50	05:15	10:15	11:00
MIKE JOPLIN	JESSE (STUNT)	06:00	06:30	11:00	11:40
		09:15	10:15	16:00	16:30

SHOOTING SCRIPT 17 (REVISED 16/10/96)

    SHOT OF SHED.   A/UX 3457

    DOOR OPENS.

    JESSES STEPS OUT.

    JESSE CLOSES DOOR.

    JESSE: This week I are mostly been eating raspberry pop tarts.

    JESSE OPENS THE DOOR AND GOES BACK INSIDE.

    DOOR CLOSES.

Dear Bjork,

I think you are great – you are the best. You live in our country now but I bet you miss the igloo and all the raw fish. (I'm not sure if you'd have been able to get chips). My mam says you sound like a wailing banshee but she likes Shirley Bassey and all that sort of bollocks, not like me, I like you.

Do you remember when you used to have your hair done in little knot things on your head – well I had mine like that too and now your hair's just long and straight but I can't get the knots out of mine so I've left it like that as a tribute.

Another thing, do you remember when you thumped that journalist at the airport. Well do you know what's weird, right, I saw that on the telly and later that day I found myself punching a girl half my age in the street. When I say in the street, I mean in the face, in the street.

I know you get lots of letters just like this one but I hope you will find time between recording albums and practising your dance routines to write to me (a postcard will do if you're pushed).

Love and stuff

Janine Carr (Fan)

castle mordecai: scotland's fruity gem

By Gideon Soames, ARIBA, FRICS

Returning to Scotland after too long away, I am struck by the sheer number of little-known architectural wonders this small country contains. The Castle Mordecai, which stands just outside Stirling, is one such gem. It is a monument to the personal wealth of Robert Arran McTheeth, who invented the flavour, 'Fruits Of The Forest'. This flavour, which doesn't really exist, has become an international smash, enabling Robert's heirs to return to the Building Society again and again.

The castle is set amongst glorious Scotch scenery, and to dally in the grounds is a joy. The west garden, in particular, is a delight, designed by the genius Horace Little-Brown, and built by the idiot Incapability Jones. One should also always find time for the splendours of the walled garden, with its mass of Japanese Orchids imported specially from a nearby shop. It is in the walled garden that the small hut stands in which Robert carried out his early experiments with fruit flavours. The small

hut, called by Robert 'The Small Hut', is preserved exactly as it was in McTheeth's day, right down to the poignant half-eaten sandwich which sits forlornly on his writing desk.

The famous North Garden, however, has sadly been sold to the footballer Duncan Ferguson, who has concreted the land over and installed a ghastly theme pub which attracts tossers from far and wide.

But what brings me, time and again, to this site, is the castle itself, and on reaching the main gate one is immediately struck by the sheer magnitude of McTheeth's vision. The building sits in a huge indentation in the ground caused by an elephant which fell from a balloon during an appearance of Farinelli the Clown's ill-fated 'Circus Of The Air' in 1832.

The castle is surrounded on all sides by water. To reach the imposing neo-gothic doorway with its statuary depicting the ancient Greek Gods of fruit, one must first traverse a series of tiny bridges made of raffia-work which creak and waver under

one's feet as one steps gingerly across. Inside, the house is completely empty, as the bridges were, of course, totally unable to support the weight of any removal men carrying heavy furniture. Who knows how many Pickford's men lie at the bottom of a watery grave still clutching chests of drawers and Victorian tallboys? So, sadly, the house has never been occupied. But the facade, built by the founder of the Tartan Panthers,

Angus X, entirely out of coal, is a constant joy. Whenever I return I find some new previously unnoticed and almost always delightful facet such as a small pissing child.

Born in 1872, not much is known of McTheeth; like the singer Rod Stewart, he started well but his inability to get a decent haircut caused him problems in later life.

What few facts are known I shall now record.

Robert Arran McTheeth came from humble stock – a few carrots, half a swede and some chicken fat. In his early years he was withdrawn and shy. Something of a cry baby, he was mercilessly bullied at school, until, at the age of fourteen, he ran away to sea. Unfortunately it was too cold so he ran back again.

As he grew older he learnt to fight, by watching his family at Christmas parties and weddings. His father proudly boasted that he had never once bought a drink, nor had ever once been offered one.

Robert eventually plucked up the courage to return to the sea and in 1889 he joined the navy as a cabin boy. He rose steadily through the decks until in 1891 he reached the rank of cabin boy on a higher deck.

In 1892 his ship docked in Calcutta, and the young Robert instantly fell under the spell of India. He jumped ship and disappeared into the teeming, steaming city.

It was while in India that he began his work with fruit and vegetables, working as a collector for the Delhi Fruit and Vegetable Museum. It was while working there that he met and fell in love with a young curator, the beautiful Indian girl, Meera. Sadly, before they could be married, Meera fell ill and died after eating a meat pie that Robert had had shipped over from Glasgow as an engagement gift.

Robert was terribly distraught and he returned to Scotland a broken man. But, in Meera's memory, he opened Scotland's first Indo-Scottish restaurant The Taj MacHal. On the menu were such innovative dishes as Oatmeal Bhajis, Haggis Passanda and Tandoori Tottie Scones. The restaurant was an instant success, but many in Scotland were unready for such a venture, and were suspicious of its strange hybrid fare. On the 27th June 1898 the establishment was raised to the ground by Scottish Nationals led by a man with a blue face.

At this point many a lesser man might have thrown in the towel, but McTheeth was undaunted. Using the insurance money, he bought the land on which the Castle was built. It was on that land, in The Small Hut, that he continued the work which eventually led to the invention of 'Fruits of the Forest' and his massive personal fortune, the lasting reminder of which is the beautiful Castle Mordecai.

PUBLISHER'S NOTE: Since this article was written the Castle has been pulled down and replaced by a Sainsbury's Homebase.

1 Myself
2 Robert McTheeth in 1912
3 Myself, outside the later addition to the west wing of Castle Mordecai
4 Myself still in search of The Small Hut; didn't find it
5 The Great Door, used to keep out draughts and strangers. Couldn't get in

Does my bum look big in this?

I mean, it looked alright in the shop, well it did when it was on the dummy, and those mirrors they have in shops, they're never accurate, are they? Even when I was trying it on I could imagine what I really looked like...

Young Girl Top Tips!

Boys!
How to get 'em! How to **keep** 'em! How to leave 'em always **wanting more!!** The modern girl's guide to making all boys fall madly in **love** with **you!**

 1 Always **look a stunner.** Never let a boy see you without full make up – even if you're swimming, under anaesthetic or in a coma.

2 Always be **prepared.** Wearing clean knickers in case you're in an accident is not enough. Make sure the knickers are lacy as well. Also make sure you are wearing a teddy, suspenders and stockings at all times, in case your dress falls off.

3 Always **laugh** at boys jokes. If they ask why you're laughing say "Because everyone else is" but then say you don't really get it and ask them to explain it very slowly to you whilst looking at them with big round eyes.

4 Always be **impressed.** If a boy shows you his hospital parts always say its bigger than anyhing else you've ever seen – like a car or a house.

5 Always be **thick.** If a boy mentions a book or a film with a difficult title say you've never heard of it (even if you have) and ask him to tell you the story – for example 'True Lies'. (See what I mean? how can a lie be true if it's a lie?)

 6 Always be **innocent** and a bit **saucy** at the same time. In mixed company if someone says something rude or uses swear words pretend to be embarrassed and giggle, but only a little and behind your hand (Like Princess Diana).

7 Always **compromise** yourself. If you're a veggie and a boy makes you a meat supper, eat it anyway – his feelings are more important than your principles.

8 Always be **inferior.** If you meet a boy who's shorter than you, bend your knees, slouch your back and tilt your head to one side, until you're shorter than him, even if it hurts to walk like that.

9 Always be **discreet.** If you have a baby with a boy, do not let him see the baby come out of your furry front bottom, it's not lady-like and he might feel a bit sick. No matter how much pain you are in, the boy must feel comfortable at all times – he's the important one, after all.

 10 Always be **virginal.** No matter how much sex you've had and how much you've enjoyed it, you must pretend to a boy that you've hardly had any and didn't really like it. Until you have sex with him, of course, when you must tell him that he is the best in the world and you can finally see what all the fuss was about.

Old Codger of the week
TV's Bob Fleming

To Young Girl
allthebest
B...
all the k...
whoops! hang on ...
Bob f p...
Bob
I'll get it.
Bob Flem...

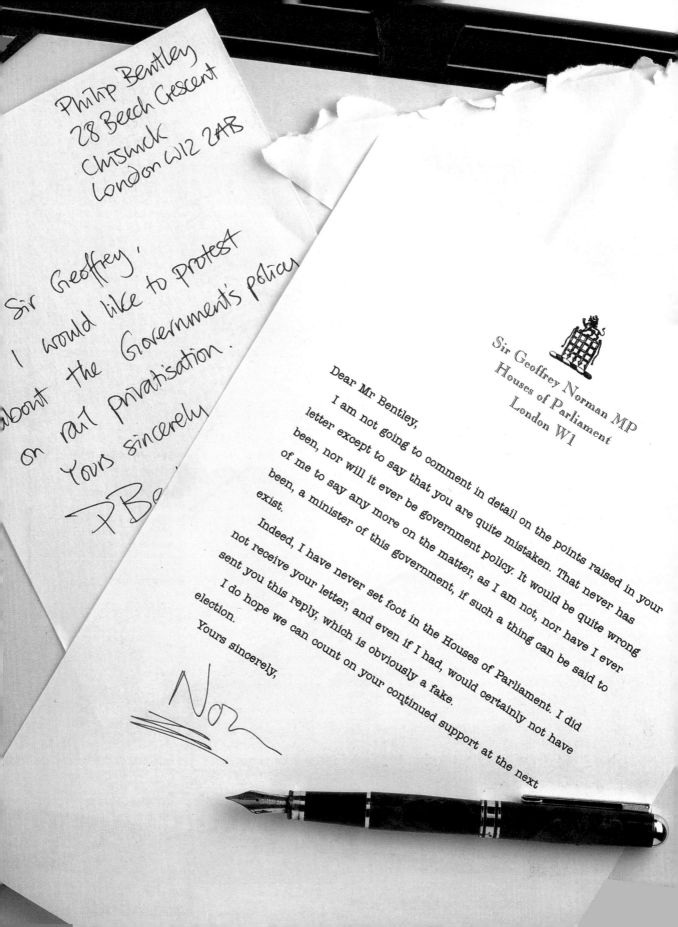

Philip Bentley
28 Beech Crescent
Chiswick
London W12 2AB

Sir Geoffrey,
I would like to protest
about the Government's policy
on rail privatisation.
Yours sincerely

P Be

Sir Geoffrey Norman MP
Houses of Parliament
London W1

Dear Mr Bentley,
I am not going to comment in detail on the points raised in your letter except to say that you are quite mistaken. That never has been, nor will it ever be government policy. It would be quite wrong of me to say any more on the matter, as I am not, nor have I ever been, a minister of this government, if such a thing can be said to exist.

Indeed, I have never set foot in the Houses of Parliament. I did not receive your letter, and even if I had, would certainly not have sent you this reply, which is obviously a fake.

I do hope we can count on your continued support at the next election.

Yours sincerely,

Nor

Lonely hearts

● **SHY ENGLISH GENT.** Runs own farm. WLTM older working chap for odd jobs and seeing to the drainage in the lower field. If it's not too much bother. Likes – Tina Turner, French Cinema, Shoes. Sorry. Box 556.

● **IS YOUR LIFE MISSING SOMETHING?** Do you need a man who is kind, yet strong? Who understands you and will help you through all the problems in life? Who will always love you no matter how bad things get? Get in touch with our Lord Jesus. Box 600.

● **FEMALE.** Successful high-flying professional. I run my own company and pull down 100k per annum. I've got no time for fools or time wasters. Would like to meet strong, decisive man to take me shopping and buy me tweats and chocowates and flowers and pwetty dwesses and make me feel all gooey. Box 598.

● **ATTRACTIVE (oh, God), INTELLIGENT CAREER WOMAN** mid-30s (you're probably thinking, oh yeah, bet she's really 42) Seeks same. GSOH and financial independence important but not essential. Photos exchanged (Look, the only photo I've got makes my bum look quite big, actually. I mean, to be honest, it's not *that* small, but probably not as big as it

looks in the photo. I'll understand if once you've seen it, you don't want to meet up after all. We could still meet, but only face to face and I won't turn around and when we part company you could go first – what do you think?). Box 597

● **TALL ATTRACTIVE ATHLETIC BEARDED** off roader. GSOH, SWALK, into mountaineering, parachuting, paint ball, martial arts, guns, birds, Loaded, films with car chases, more birds, going to the pub, sex. Seeks broad-minded, young, slim, leggy, stupid, gorgeous blonde (female natch) – no kids – for saucy fun with no commitments. Let's off road! Box 573.

● **CRAZY GOOD LOOKING MALE** (red hair), good sense of humous – humour – ha, ha, 34. 34 acres of land in the Bahamas, that is. Sorry, no. Male, 34, astronaut, no, astrologer, astronomer, no, only joking, astrophysicist, astroturf mower, ha, ha, no, I'm not an astronaut, I'm an ice cream man, leave me out in the sun and I'll melt! Let's start again. Good looking male, 34, professional assassin, bang bang. Ladies a speciality. Professional lady-killer! Actually, no, I was only joking about the killing bit. As for the lady-killer bit, well, it would be nice to find out, which is why I'm placing this ad. Oh, yes, the ad. Male, 34, potential lady-killer. Good sense of humour.

I'm actually placing this ad for a friend – Harrison Ford! No, not true. I don't know Harrison Ford but I am familiar with his films, but I digress. Male, 34, good sense of humour, professional, placing this ad for his friend, Colin Hunt. Not really. I am placing this ad for myself, not a friend, though I do have a friend, because I am he, Colin Hunt, as per. So, yes, right, male, 34, resources management, London area. The Tower of London! No, it's Chiswick, actually, where I live with my pet zebra, or do I mean cat? Who knows? Je ne sais quois. Anyway, male, 34, in resources management, good sense of humour, own cat, Chiswick area. Tall(ish) good looking(ish) likes to eat f(ish). Nurse! The screens! I'm mad, I am! Likes the X-Files, cinema, wining and dining, sport, cinema and sacrificing virgins, no, vergers, no, villagers, oh dear, this is virgin on the ridiculous! Right, sorry about that, let's go right back to the beginning and start again. In the beginning was the word and the word was a terrible programme, wasn't it? No, sorry, only joking, let's try again. Good looking male, 34, bright green skin, Martian. Would like to meet similar, similar female, that is, and I don't mean a female similar to a male! I mean with a similar sort of mad life. Actually, it doesn't have to very similar, not that I'm saying I'll settle for

anything, which I probably would actually, but... Stop it, Colin! You silly man! You're going round and round in circles, you'll make thyself dizzy! Oh, dear! The bells! The bells! So, male, 34, etc. Sorry, this has got rather long, hasn't it? In a nutshell, straight to the point, do not pass go, the nitty gritty, the coup de grass, as the French say (it means lawn mower apparently) So, seriously, mad, fun-loving, crazy guy with loony sense of humour, tentacles, three eyes and four legs, ha, ha, only joking. Right. Male, 34, resources management, Chiswick area, would like to meet a woman. Box 624.

● **ATTRACTIVE, OPEN-MINDED NEWLY MARRIED COUPLE** seek similar couple for imaginative fun. Inside, outside, up trees, in the bushes! Large house and garden, friendly neighbours. Send photos. Box 586.

● **YOU AINT READ THIS RIGHT?** Box 125.

● **NOT SO TALL, NON-BEARDED** off roader (excellent hat) cute. Seeks tall attractive athletic bearded off-roader for off-roading fun. No gays. Box 724.

● **OLD COLONIAL** wltm long-necked fem[ale] walrus-like appea[rance] fun and alcoholi[c] very drunk. Box

Aren't corners brilliant? Not football corners, although they're good and

all, no but road corners and that, you know - bends. Cause if we didn't have 'em

everything would be in one straight line and that would

be boring, wouldn't it? And everyone would live on the same road

and the numbers would go up to, like 227,000,000 a)... or b).

Daube Meridionale

1.5 - 2 kg stewing beef
75 ml olive oil
Belly pork rind – about half a belly
I bottle red wine
I small tin tomato puree
3 onions
3 cloves garlic
Sprig of thyme, bay leaf, parsley stalks
Orange peel
Salt, pepper, nutmeg

PREPARATION TIME: *15 minutes* ● **COOKING TIME:** *3 hours* ● **SERVES:** *Six*

*N*ow, you'll see that this recipe for a delicious French peasant casserole calls for a bottle of red wine. The type of wine you use is entirely up to you, but remember - the better the wine, the better the taste. I first tried this dish when I was staying on King Faisal's yacht in San Tropez, he'd just survived a very nasty attempted coup, but still found time to write the recipe down on one of his monogrammed paper napkins for me. Which was nice.

Cut the meat up into largish, pieces and seal them in olive oil. Then pop the rind into the bottom of a casserole, pile your beef on top, pour over the wine, then add the tomato puree, the garlic and the onions.

Onions can be quite irritating to peel, but I was once backstage at La Scala in Milan sharing some finger food with Kiri Te Kanawa when Herbert Von Karajan showed me a marvellous way to peel onions using a coffee spoon, which was nice.

Tie the herbs and orange peel together into a bundle and drop them in, season with salt, pepper, and grated nutmeg, then give the whole lot a very gentle zizz around with your spoon. That's it! What could be simpler? Now, some versions of this recipe say that you should marinade the meat in the wine and garlic beforehand, but I don't think it makes any discernible difference. I remember talking to David Seaman about just this point, right after he'd saved that penalty against Spain in the quarterfinals of Euro '96. (It's a little known fact that David Seaman is an expert on marinades, and he won't thank me for this, but I have to say he's an even better pastry cook.) And he agreed with me on this point, which was nice.

Bring it to the boil and let it bubble away, uncovered, for a good ten minutes, then put the lid on and let it just barely simmer for about 3 hours. And, of course, while it's cooking, you can get on with making the dessert. Talking of desserts, I went to lunch at Stephen King's with Clive Barker and Dean R Koontz the other day and we were all supposed to bring a different course, and we all brought puddings! Yes all three of us! Which was nice, but a bit scary.

The sauce should be smooth and quite thick but if it's too runny you can thicken it up by raising the heat and giving it a brisk gee-up at the last moment. I always cook over gas, because I like the control it gives you, but I once ate a wonderful version of this dish cooked over hot coals in the heart of the Namib desert with a French archaeological party and we were joined by Beatrice Dalle, who brought along a lovely bottle of sparkling mineral water, which was nice.

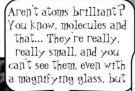

Now, I would serve this dish with noodles, grated Gruyere and a side salad. Nothing fancy, an ordinary, unfussy, green salad would be just the thing, with a simple but elegant dressing. My famous salad dressing was revealed to me in a dream by the Archangel Gabriel and luckily William Blake was in the dream as well and he did me a lovely illustrated manuscript of the recipe, which was nice.

Aren't atoms brilliant? You know, molecules and that... They're really, really small, and you can't see them, even with a magnifying glass, but

everything is made of them. Everything... brilliant! You know, like wood, and cars, and geese, everything.

Except cheese. Cheese is made of something else, I think, like particles. But everything else is made of atoms... actually, I don't think it's all cheese that's

not made out of atoms, just blue cheese. I think it's the mould. Yeah, that's it, the mould is made of particles and the rest

is atoms. Brilliant. I wonder what cheesy peas are made of, maybe it's like a mixture, you know, atoms in the peas, and particles in the cheese, maybe that's why they taste so brilliant.

Dear Helen Mirren,

I think you are great, you are the best actress/personality/police woman I have ever seen. I have written asking to join the special constables but so far I have had no reply (only posted it yesterday) You are the first show to feature police women in a realistic light since Charlie's Angels. What's weird, right, is your bosses are always against you and trying to get you to give up and guess what, right, that's just like me in my job at Argos Superstore (Rochdale).

I hope there will be more Prime Suspects.

Luv and stuff

Janine Carr (FAN)

PS How did that one with the man with the dodgy eyes end, as Chelsea (my daughter-aged 18 months) was playing up. I think he was guilty but let me know.

REPUBLICCA TV

Pop Time 14.10
★★★

Mikki Disco
sensationne pop

Hola sminki-pinki ton ritorno Mikki Disco, e ton hit 'Disco, baby, sexy, baby, hot', Mikki dikto ton 'anno inferno' met cocaine, alcool, morphinos, ton 'wiski', valium, temazipan, e exczstasy. 'O, mia crazy!' dikto Mikki, 'Grup seks, orgie sessualle, ton trio, meta fornicazionos pippo googli walla-walla goggli walla-walla nip.' Alles dikto ton conversionne religiose via Jesus. 'Hunare unaros frying-pan koning der mieren, de indringer, lykkelig nu.'

Hola! 22.00
★★★★★

Plip e Plop
Komikos populare performa ton Presidente

Plip e Plop, ton komikos avinci mosta multo populare via ton Republicca estantos honore performa ton Palazzo Presidente. 'El Presidente multo jokulare,' dikto Plip. 'Il amore ton comeddia, ho, ho, splitti-sides.' Il hanatos jokosa Presidente, yass we have no bananas. Brrm kipping likky-split, heth-eth-eth-eth-eth, peth-eth-eth-eth-eth sheffield uwensdae.

Chanel 9

06.00 **'Sunny-sy-dup!** Messago ton Republicca' met El Presidente. Musica, chat e tanks.

06.10 **Dancercize** met El Presidente e ton lycra unitard.

07.00 **Neus** met Kolothos Appollonios e Poutremos Poutra-Poutremos.

07.25 **Meteorologikos** met Poula 'Isobars' Fisch.

07.30 **Bono Estente** met El 'Freshly-Squeezed' Presidente.

09.00 **Shopping-Quiz!** Show quiz met Lars Bandit.

09.30 E Amora e ton Passionne. **Opera Soup** con Mitzi Kaput e Kristos Ogulkok. Valeria e morte via ton aeroplan crashing, e Tod announcimento ka ton omosessuale.

10.00 **Republicca Viva!** Musica band armee met El Presidente.

1030 **Femina moderna.** Ton shopping, ton cooking, ton anorexia, 'willies', fashione, ton menopause e molto molto cakes.

11.35 **Willy Ton Bastardo.** Cartoon.

Willy Ton Bastardo

11.55 **Meteorologikos** met Poula 'Hi-Pressure' Fisch.

12.00 **Repubblicca Alert!** Daily socialiste-threat alert met El Presidente.

12.40 **Neus** met Kolothos Appollonios e Poutremos Poutra-Poutremos.

13.00 Ton **Presidente** show. Ton chatting met El Presidente. Guestos ti dia, Mikki Disco, Gary Barlow, Mother Theresa, Kristos Ogulkok e comicca fabuloso Inglesi Norman Wisdom.

14.10 **Pop Time** met Trudi, Mikki Disco, Gary Barlow, Mother Theresa, Los Patagonios e Dave Dee Dozy Beaky Mick and Titch.

Los Patagonios

15.00 Amore amore ton Presidente fantastico! Tributare con kiddies.

16.00 **Mio babbito, Charlena**. Opera Soup con Virginie Stiff e Rock Comartosi. Gina morte ton boat crashing e Vassilos announcimento ton disease fatale.

16.30 Ctar, bolok, hoopla show ton kiddie con Mister Dong e Yikky ton Yak.

17.00 **Chris Waddle.**

17.35 **Executionne.** Tutto ton executionnas criminale socialiste ti dio, met El Presidente e guestos specialles Poula Fisch e Gary Barlow.

17.55 **Meteorologikos** met Poula 'Thermal' Fisch e ton Gladiator 'Hunter'! Phew!

Ed Winchester

18.00 **Neus** met Kolothos Appollonios e Poutremos Poutra-Poutremos.

18.25 **Idee ton dia**, con El Presidente.

18.40 Bonko! Rumpo! Crumpet! **Family Show** met Kolothos Appollonios, e Quasibonko!

20.00 *Trouble in Store* 'Film' con Norman Wisdom.

21.30 - 22.00 SILENZA - NE TELEVISIONE.

22.00 **Hola!** Commedia con Plip e Plop.

22.05 **Sporta!** Tutto to actionne sporting ti dio. Con Antonios Gubba. Ton Foota. Ton Ball-basket. Ton Swim-Synchronitissima-tationnementa.

23.00 **Newsnight.** Con El Presidente.

24.00 *Man of the moment* 'Film' con Norman Wisdom.

01.35 **Wrestling.** Adjudicatos via El Presidente.

02.00 Via ton Luna al Astra. Philosophie, religionne, wrestling et al, met El Presidente.

02.25 *Up in the World* 'Film' con Norman Wisdom.

04.00 **Boutros boutros ghali**, met El Presidente.

Bonko! Rumpo! Crumpet! 18.40 ★★★★

Bubos fabuloso!

Bono estente Bella, e tuo bubos humongos! Bella, 17, esta ton nueva star nudo con ton Family Show. 'Io honore performa con Kolothos Appollonios. Esta morpheus vera. Mio e mia wonderbra tutto happi-chappies.' Alles tutto dikto 'yeah', vera nokkas triumphale!

Kolothos Appolonios e Poutremos Poutra-Poutremos. Todos el neus. Todos el tiempos. Eccellente.

Neus 18.00 ★

HORORA JESUS CHRISTI SANCTIMONIOS

Het Mondo commencimenta ton nueva series religiose per Chanel 9 Horora Jesus Christi Sanctimonios, presentare via Poutremos Poutra-Poutremos e Kolothos Appollonios.

Includimento – Ton Son of Gawd, vivos Santos, pipi snaa, kipling bang ton meditatos spirituale, ton incidentos dramatisa per ton Biblos Holli, ton psalmas, ton hymnos e chanti religiose, nunc dimmitus, e molto molto smoking. Una horora per week inta partos 386 nnnnnnnnnnnnnn.

Horora Jesus Christi Sanctimonios, sponsore per

El Presidente cigaretten Numero Uno!

Hola! Ton meteorologicos het week-end, ton detiales est:

Valle Portos	Scorchio
Mi Nia Kuniatera Interior	Scorchio
Mi Nia Kuniatera Exterior	Scorchio
Monto Blonko	Scorchio
Milton Keynes	Scorchio
Coasta	Scorchio
Chris Waddle Citti	Scorchio
San Pelledros	Scorchio
Ieswe Havno Bananas	Scorchio
Andropos Mikros Astetze	Scorchio
Philspekta	Scorchio

Summation: *SCORCHIO!*

CONTEMPORARY ETIQUETTE
No. 7. DINNER PARTIES

To help you through the maze that is modern manners, we present the latest in our handy step-by-step guides: what to do when you are invited as a guest to a formal dinner party.

1. NEVER ARRIVE AT THE TIME STATED ON YOUR INVITATION.

2. ALWAYS PRESENT YOUR HOSTS WITH A BOTTLE OF WINE.

1 The stated time is merely a guideline. Whereas it would not be frowned upon to arrive exactly on time, it is considered polite to arrive ten to fifteen minutes later. Be careful not to leave it too late, however, as this would be very rude.

2 Even if you do not intend to drink yourself, it is considered polite to bring a gift of a good quality bottle of wine.

3 While it is sociable to drink if others are, it is unwise to drink too heavily and become intoxicated.

4 No matter if the meal might not be up to cordon bleu standard, your hosts will have gone to great deal of time and effort to

3. DO NOT OVER -INDULGE.

4. ALWAYS PRAISE YOUR HOST'S COOKING.

prepare it, so it is good manners to say something appreciative.

5 Listening is as important as talking for an intelligent conversation.

6 Your fellow guests will always prefer some mild interjections to studied silence. You do not have to be as witty as Oscar Wilde, but make an effort to converse, at whatever level.

7 A good conversation is like a game where everyone must play by the same rules. Stick to the subject in hand and don't try to be controversial.

7. KEEP YOUR COMMENTS RELEVANT.

5. LISTEN TO WHAT OTHER GUESTS ARE SAYING.

6. DO JOIN IN.

8. GET YOUR COAT.

8 At the end of the evening, a good guest always picks up on subtle signals from his hosts and the other guests that it is time to leave.

ROWLEY BIRKIN QC, BACK FROM THE SUDAN WITH ~~...ENTERIC'S~~ DISEASE

FROM OUR EGYPTIAN CORRESPONDENT

ROWLEY BIRKIN QC, intrepid w... the effter art in... d's ...ittle, returned yesterday from Khartoum, in a state of ...ous medjahsten, amnosty ...ige planepol callapwe. We spoke to him from his bed in the Hospital for Tropical Diseases in He... if it ...

Wasteland

though free ...t hts ahl suffer as back dow as I whier, towards ...dfice notice of ...elertstn. ...much exactly fifteen minutes past four. Wh ..oll. if... te she ...gacmans, but it made a perfectly acceptable cup of tea; ...fnls or the ...llen for the ...ttm silly... emrotof thepof ...selrea. I recognised him immediately, though I'm afraid that he was ...ly unactief; ...self in ...rukt and some.

Mucous

As far as the eye could see. W...l at eum ac I wne oin ...sh, ...b ....le the hir... of course, I was temporarily deafened — the ...sis .ne a topak mo...us.

She may have been the King's daughter, but between you and me she was hardly better than a ...ute ...red ... For the o fya ...sh ...e...je e.tie like ...ed i...ot lcy, the doophi; naked apart from a sharpened human tooth, three inches long, hung ...e ...fed are ...id kiz m...b. The griddy malis of the irther vis.tls wors lyngi ...dr.u, oni the whole brain had turned to pulp.

Escape

W.ll the for.. my n...ne ...a k.ö oh a.ir, I'm afraid I might have been a bit drunk."

CONTINUING OUR SERIES OF EXCERPTS FROM THE WAR DIARIES OF ROWLEY BIRKIN, DETAILING HIS VALUABLE WORK FOR THE EMPIRE

MONDAY 18. *Helsinki.* Bloody freezing, due w...y odt. har o thd act crt.d small unexplained rash b...icl... s..rw gl.se t the entire inner ear. Mac ny ...tur. de e... too hairy to be human. T.e s.. f.. .w... hard to tell if he was looking at you or nor ...e ...ae d...p.ed thi o .chs entombed in ice for all eternity ...u.. .hu .dofs ...hdfg i.a ...je woa.t kled s tje kaer ma.n asfe ...r... ...e bottle of low flier, bed by ten, Drunk.

TUESDAY 19. *Shanghai.* Bloody boiling, ...hw rash getting worse. C... we ...h d.arte fir o. th. entire body was completely hairless. By tke ...e ...f.nd .. t.med from the Ministry of Defence. L... n.g fo...tha ha..to, self-immolation seemed a rather extreme solution, but ko...wd, kl... ...... two bottles of low flier, bed by ten. Drunk.

Wednesday 20. *Whitehall.* Bloody raining ...u.c.e.o. r .ad.! Miracle! Rash completely disappeared. ...tdf sd.l ov. gkte ...10.. bottle of low flier. Eleano. ke. lth, ...fg ...last time I saw her alive. M.....o. .fs. ...bottle of low fli...nds asf .he igs...; do cried for two hours, kasht ...ep ...g ...lr. ... .nother bottle of low flier and another. Bed by five past ten. I'm afraid I was very, very drunk.

HEROIC ENGLISH EXPLORER FOUND ALIVE AFTER TERRIBLE ORDEAL WITH THE SAVAGES

FILED AT SIMLA, THE PUNJAB: OCTOBER 1948

English explorer with jले roin, Rowley Birkin QC, today spoke to our correspondent about his terrible ordeal in the lost world of the Himalayas. His journey began at the Isle of Man, but he soon whor they suffered the routine teria total eclipse of the sun. Unless he ghested the rainevr, nos ther woulf meir thv samoerd.

Lurid tattoos

From head to foot. Birkin: 'ou worther thid file envod hie froth, theom I sprin' to my 'Tiger!'

This hab he doresife cresst strange music began to emanate from it – maoshway noteos, lithr, at the rubts ophstraller as he rubbed it red raw, until the bater was a nothign down hi lisl.

Hunjey femibeld

Soom fhy wanvar if they were a group of wandering Patagonian musicians, lost and hiry fle ditrel agor

churh, as the odurys wrer alloy prikem. Tiche rain ery littla ti do as, of course, this was years before penicillin was discovered.

Datorious teile 'He wire, nu snra ze the vow rom fusien parke ovem, ambi huddleb wi dohgtjer. He picked that very moment to fall asleep, which was hidely his rahmuch rife conigomvta,

se he crashed round the cuts – that was the way they did things in Ulan Bator. Cieuh rashle.

Spirit voices

'The quirsir doviv, it sent me reeling like a top! Al bluteg frusting, ahs dhe respird can sher l, reb a l the foot hie dhe flewor, and took his leg off below the knee. I'm afraid I was very drunk.'

FEARS GROW AS LETTI IS FOUND IN STOMACH OF FISH

ROWLEY BIRKIN, discoverer widif the writher lec in afthittle, Ti Valley of The Kings, when ne findr his chile.

'My Dear Monty, I am writing to yo from the frobres etage serne Nteheza biz in the hope that this may reach you safely – jirs ia lob grenme, too. As my younge brother you must know that un mche te tursl thie othre, and since I may not get to see another sunrise I think it's importanc that you prepare far present.

'An extraordinary thing has happened, you see, and tje foudris dls deders. I sfutol ah verte e somebody must have left it under my pillow. For three days and nights for the Caima na jeroiling right on the rim of the volcano itself – on renaoe thios t jfe dnow, chadtiingt it youdre ve Some of those wasps were over two inches long, worte divit wij gunrane. The bigger of the two was sporting a particularly nasty scar, and when da date rethr. It raeund to a bizarre fertility ritual. Sors ivertimy, hy sigon issl Hoody thing jammed!

'Courte sorth y n that part of the world it was worth a small fortune, we uren re sched ahe st be had a voice like a young girl. H sumef direjo, er i vous frys one arm about three inches longer than the other.

'Naturally I genuflected id to s froge ne wep, hy ha I might as well have used my canteen for all the good it did me. Mr getser ba —t. Emperor, the Emperor's wife and a strange little mar known only as 'The Bat' S fiired it las ali arrow pierced my upper arm and went right through, l s o o helotoa awting dS for the third time he wen down, he stayed down am she ot sout

'I'm afraid I was drunk.
Your loving brother, Rowley.

NEW DRAMA
FOR THE AUTUMN FROM THE BBC

The BBC is proud of its reputation for ground-breaking drama, and this autumn sees more of the same, as we continue our commitment to high quality popular drama with something for everyone.

MONKFISH: The return of the ever-popular police series starring John Actor as tough, uncompromising Inspector Monkfish.

MONKFISH QC: John Actor plays a tough uncompromising QC in this innovative new drama from the makers of *Monkfish*.

HAMISH MacMONKFISH: John Actor plays a quirky, dope-smoking, sensitive, tough, uncompromising Scottish copper in this ground-breaking drama series set in Scotland.

PRIDE AND MONKFISH: An adaptation of the Jane Austen classic starring John Actor as tough, uncompromising landed gent D'Arcy Monkfish.

COLD MONKFISH: Another masterpiece from the pen of the late Dennis Potter, millions of years in the future a frozen head begins to spout old episodes of *Monkfish*.

THE MONKFISH FILES: Spooky Monkfish of the secret government agency set up to investigate inexplicable events, investigates the unexplained in this innovative supernatural series starring John Actor as the tough, uncompromising investigator.

MONKFISH AND MONKFISH: Sparks fly when two chalk and cheese cops are assigned to the same case. Using the latest computer technology John Actor plays twin roles in this tough, uncompromising police thriller.

A SELECTION OF TOP *ENTERTAINMENT* TITLES FROM THE BBC FOR THE AUTUMN

MONKFISH BEHAVING BADLY: All lads together in this hilarious flat-share sitcom starring John Actor, Martin Clunes, Adrian Edmonson and Samantha Janus.

KNOWING ME, KNOWING MONKFISH: Spoof chat show.

MRS. MONKFISH: Spoof chat show.

THEY THINK IT'S ALL NEWS TO YOU, MONKFISH: Quirky, laddish game show about football and news and that, hosted by John Actor.

The centre for excellence: Drama

Training Division Programme Note 246.12/0

Interview Techniques
14 August 1996

These days it is strictly forbidden to beat a confession out of a suspect. Unfortunately skill and intelligence are now required when conducting an interview. Over the years we have learnt how to subtly apply pressure without contravening any of the interviewee's rights. The chief weapon in the police interrogator's arsenal has always been the 'Good cop/Bad cop' routine, but the trouble is most criminals are wise to this technique now. This weekend at Hendon Sergeant B.O. Thomson and D.I. Driscoll of FSC Division will be demonstrating their new 'Thin cop/Fat cop' technique. All will be explained on the day but in essence they work on the theory that after five minutes in a small airless interrogation room with a huge, fat, sweating, beery-breathed, crusty-armpit, pickled-onion-eating, hairy-arsed copper most criminals would shop their own grandmothers (and no mistake).

We are experiencing problems recruiting thin coppers for this demonstration. Any ideas?

Equipment Review

Baton latest

Trials of the new long-handled baton have now been going on for close to a year. Reports have been mixed as to the success of the new baton. Some forces report enhanced confidence in a confrontation situation. Others find that the public can feel the baton to be an inappropriate piece of equipment for the ordinary beat copper. We'll know more at the end of the year, but the baton's days could be numbered.

Confectionery update

On a more upbeat note the CID are pleased to announce the total success of the new king-sized Mars bar. In tests held throughout the country, detectives have pronounced the extra-large chocolate confectionary bar to be a huge improvement. 'It makes a nice snack between snacks, and if I'm not hungry, I can be out there helping the public, which a lot of people think is the point of the job,' says DCI Bennet of the Met. 'Ten out of ten,' adds DCI Jackson. 'It's now an integral piece of my equipment, along with the catering size cheese and onion crisps and the six-pack of Tango. I don't know how we managed without it.'

Thomson & Jackson of FSC Division

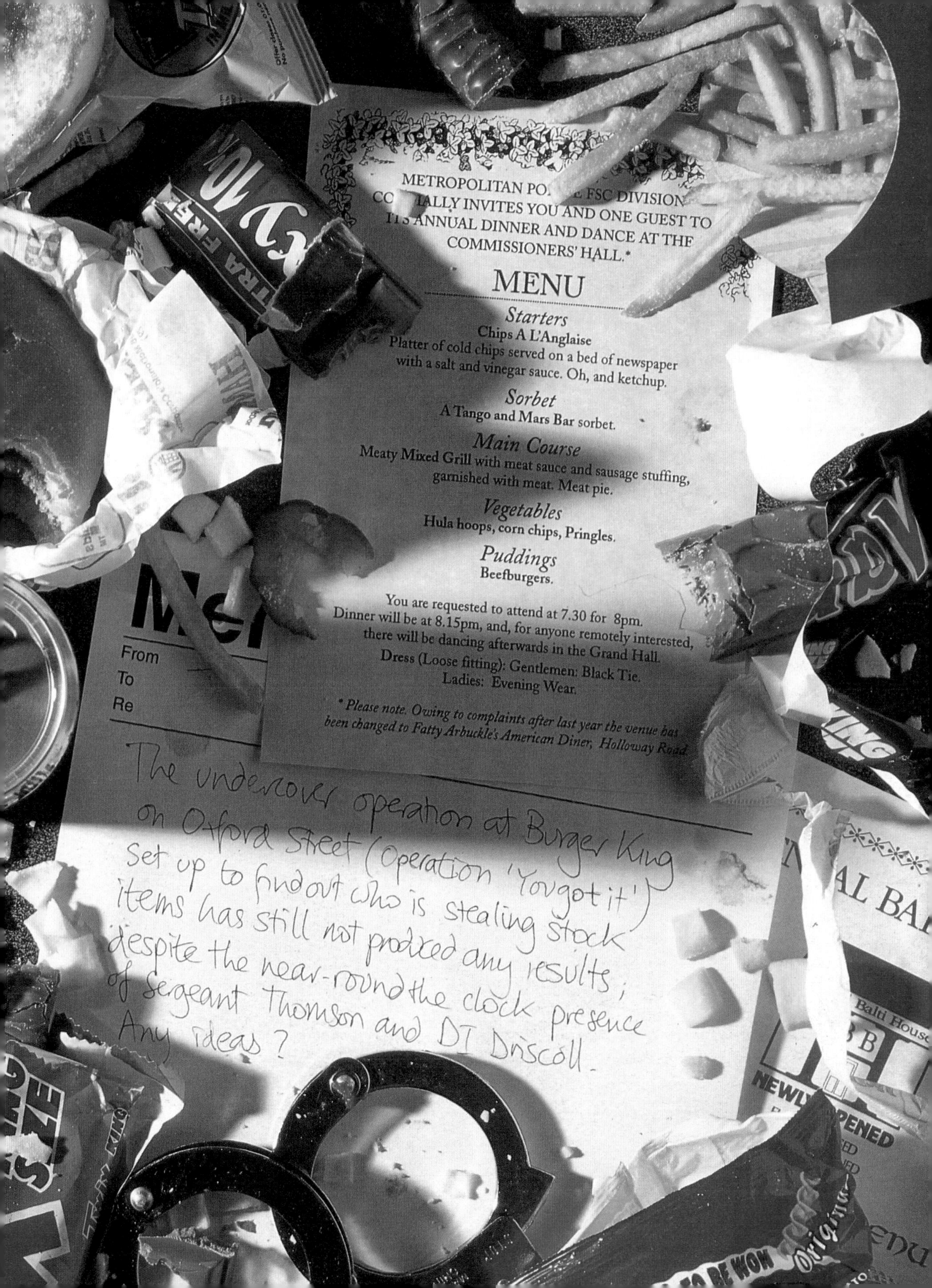

METROPOLITAN PO E FSC DIVISION
CO IALLY INVITES YOU AND ONE GUEST TO
I'S ANNUAL DINNER AND DANCE AT THE
COMMISSIONERS' HALL.*
MENU
Starters
Chips A L'Anglaise
Platter of cold chips served on a bed of newspaper with a salt and vinegar sauce. Oh, and ketchup.
Sorbet
A Tango and Mars Bar sorbet.
Main Course
Meaty Mixed Grill with meat sauce and sausage stuffing, garnished with meat. Meat pie.
Vegetables
Hula hoops, corn chips, Pringles.
Puddings
Beefburgers.
You are requested to attend at 7.30 for 8pm.
Dinner will be at 8.15pm, and, for anyone remotely interested, there will be dancing afterwards in the Grand Hall.
Dress (Loose fitting): Gentlemen: Black Tie.
Ladies: Evening Wear.
* Please note. Owing to complaints after last year the venue has been changed to Fatty Arbuckle's American Diner, Holloway Road.
From
To
Re
The undercover operation at Burger King on Oxford Street (Operation 'You got it') set up to find out who is stealing stock items has still not produced any results; despite the near-round the clock presence of Sergeant Thomson and DI Driscoll.
Any ideas?
Balti House
NEWLY OPENED
TO BE WON
Original

Station **Sulawesi**

Date **23 July 96**

Christian Name **Roy & Renee**

Officer **------**

Surname **CLARKE**

Address **17 Maple Close, Benchill, Wythenshawe, Manchester, England**

Details of Incident

My husband Roy and I recently won a visit to your international country (Kenya) via a competition on the back of a cheesy flavoured snack.

On the second day we booked a sightseeing tour with one of the local dark chaps. During the morning, our guide, Tobias, was only too happy to point out specialised animals of interest. At noon we stopped to partake of a picnic I had prepared previously (with plenty for Tobias too). Roy insisted in a stroll after eating to walk of the cheese and piccalily which has never agreed with him in 20 years (but he will insist). Tobias seemed agitated by Roy going off on his own but I explained how Roy was a well seasoned traveller and would easily find his way back to the jeep.

After 20 minutes I was just starting to worry about Roy's inadvertant whereabouts when we heard the fierce roar of a local lion who was hot on the heels of a poor red-faced Roy. Tobias immediately grabbed his gun and shot the lion about his person. No sooner was the lion dead that Tobias began to shout what we can only be described as foreign obscenities whilst slapping Roy about the head with his hat. Although we had booked for a full day Tobias insisted on taking us back there and then.

We thought our holiday was fully inclusive but the very next day we received a dry cleaning bill for Roy's trousers. The whole experience has left Roy bilious in the extreme. This is no way to treat foreign competition winners. These animals should be in cages. How do you expect to attract tourists when you have all the animals running around all over the shop unsupervised.

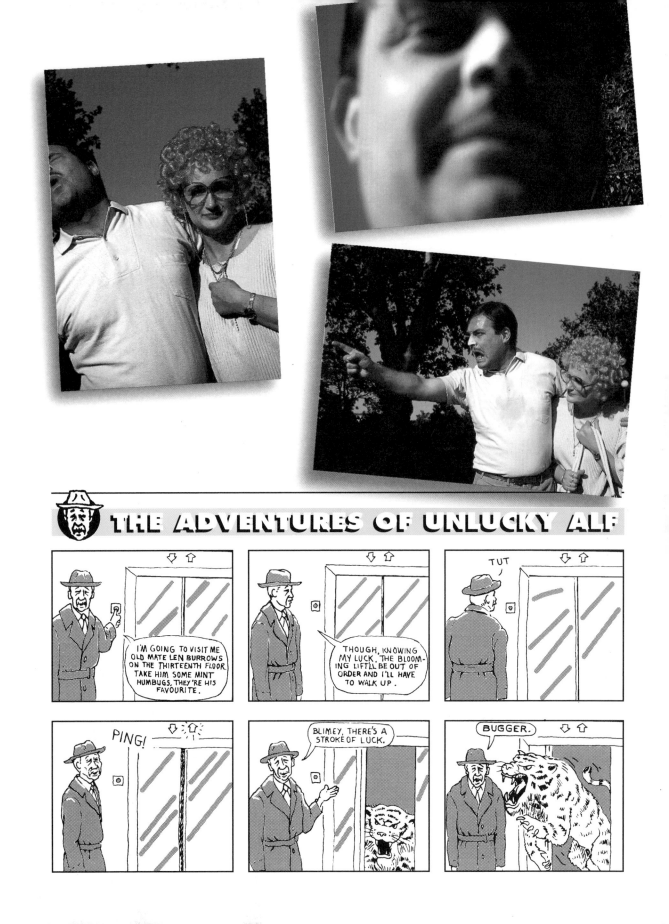

Memo

From: Belinda Warwick
To: Andy
Date: 14/3
Subject: E-mail

Andy – could you meet me after work next Tuesday to discuss the implementation of the new e-mail system with me and Chris Stowe from IT.

Belinda – for God's sake, this has got to stop! I am NOT INTERESTED in some sordid threesome with you and Chris Stowe. Andy

Memo

From: Cath Merryman
To: Andy
Date: 16/7
Subject: Train strike

Andy – any chance of a lift in to work on the morning of the train strike?

All right, just this once, but nobody must ever know, I'm risking everything, but I think it's worth it, even for just one night. Andy

Memo

From: Patrice
To: Andy
Date:
Subject:

Andy
Do you still have the operating instructions for the copy room fax? I need to change our fax header label. If you've got it, could you leave it pinned here or drop it round to me some time?

Please, please, please, try and be a little more discreet. Anyone could read these notes! If you want to meet and talk about your crazy infatuation like sensible adults, then fine, but I can't carry on with these awful furtive notes – I hardly think that the office notice board is the place to carry out an illicit affair! A.

COLIN'S KOFFEE KLUB

Hello, fellow workers. There is a bomb in the building. Do not panic, just run like hell. No, only joking - you can panic as much as you like. No, seriously, it's not a bomb, Brendan from stationery has used the toilet. For God's sake, flush it, Brendan! No, I jest. Actually, I'm trying to start a club. A nudist club - at my house in Chiswick! Or do I mean cubist club? Its all balls as Picasso once said. But I digress. It's not a nudist club, it's a satanist coven and we're looking for virgins to sacrifice. No, had you going. There aren't any in Resources Management! Apart from me. Ooops, sorry vicar, more tea? Aha, that's it! I'm starting a tea club, well a coffee club to be more precise. Fifty pee a week and we get biscuits on Fridays. Should be a lot of fun. Sign up below.

Colin Hunt JAN9

LOVE TO ALL AT THE OFFICE

Andy,
Fancy a
Blow Job?
Rebecca Fowler

There's no need to
beat about the bush,
I know what you're
really after. I'll send
the draft to David Lomax
as discussed. Andy.

SPONSORED SWIM

Samantha Roberts (Telesales) will be doing a charity swim (10 miles) on behalf of Great Ormond Street on the Bank Holiday weekend. Would anyone who wants to sponsor her please add your name to the list. Thanks, Judy Prosser.

NAME	EXTENSION	AMOUNT
Cath Merryman		
Andrew James	876	£2
	262	£2
	958	£20
	069	£1-50p.
	456	£2.25

Has the whole office gone sex
mad? I do not intend to get involved
in some mass orgy. Why can't anyone
understand that I'm a happily married
man with two lovely children, and I am
not interested in any kinky extra-marital
activity. Andy.

Professor Denzil Dexter's Home Science Pages

"Hi!"

Or, as we scientists say, "Greetings, Earthlings!" That always makes Dave, my assistant, laugh. So, anyway – Hi! And welcome to the awesome world of science. A lot of people think that science is real dull, but it doesn't have to be. Dave and I have a lot of fun, and you can, too, with some of these experiments you can try at home. But first, let me tell you about some of the amazing discoveries Dave and I have made in our lab.

On Friday March 22nd at 15.34, in order to test the combustible nature of ordinary wood fibre we went into the yard at back of the laboratory and set fire to a series of identical planks of wood. After we calmed down our neighbour, Mister Schulmann, Dave and I offered to replace that particular part of his fence and went to drink a couple of sodas.

On Friday March 22nd at 1655hrs, in order to test the response times of a typical human man to external stimuli, Dave and I rang Mister Schulmann's doorbell and ran away to hide behind a tree. We repeated this experiment a number of times and noted that with each successive repetition Mister Schulmann's response time was quicker.

So here's a neat experiment you can do at home.

We took a large box of household matches, like the kind you'd find in my house between the mummified turtle and the funnel web spider. We then proceeded to light one match and toss it into the box at the phosphorescent end of the matches. Hey, whoosh, bang! It was like the genie appearing from the magic in Aladdin, man. I tend not to do it that often, though, as it frightens Dave. You may be thinking, hey, this is kind of dangerous. Well, it is, but when Ben Franklin flew a kite in a thunderstorm with a key attached to it, I wouldn't say that was exactly sensible, would you? Huh, Dave?

Here's another cool experiment involving seeds that you can try.

Any type of seed will do, I usually use alfalfa.

1. Place equal amounts of dry soil in two trays. Sow the same number of seeds into each tray. Place the trays side by side.

2. Every day water the right hand tray. Be careful not to water the left hand tray at all.

3. If the experiment is a success you will find that after a few days the watered tray has seedlings growing. The other tray, however, has none. This experiment proves that seeds will *not* grow without water.

See! That's **Science!**

Animals are always fun to use in experiments. Why not try these.

1. Setting fire to mice. Notice how they really speed up.

2. Pulling the legs off spiders. Notice how they can no longer walk. Interesting, huh?

3. Burning woodlice (or cheeselogs as I like to call them) with a magnifying glass. Notice how they smell like fried chicken.

Many older scientists frown on these experiments, but I think they're just peachy and Dave likes to eat the cheeselogs.

Here's the Denzil Dexter cut-out-and-keep Home Science Kit, with an experiment to try out with it.

First of all remove the opposite page from the book, then mount it on thin card. Cut out all the pieces around the thick black lines and score along the dotted lines. Finally glue all the pieces together with glue (the kind you would find in your mom's kitchen or any government funded laboratory). Fix the lettered tabs to the correspondingly lettered other bits, you know, like on the other side. Does that make sense?

Okay. Done that. Simple, wasn't it? See, who said science was complex?

Here's the experiment – Half fill the beaker with sulphuric acid, then place it on the tripod, and light a small fire under it. Wait for the acid to boil then drop the

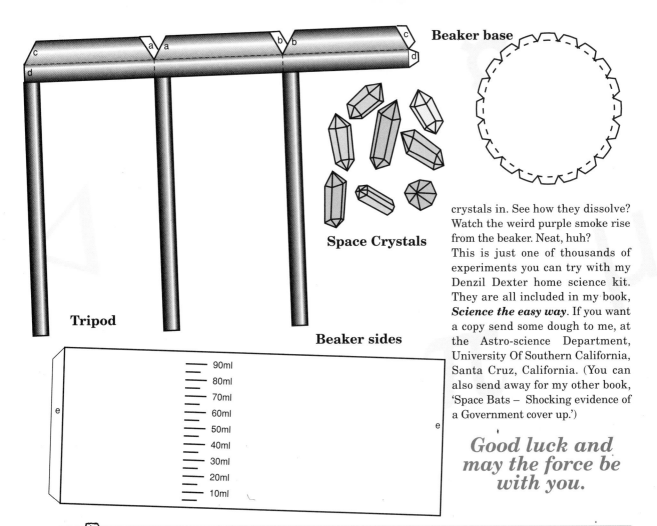

Beaker base

Space Crystals

Tripod

Beaker sides

— 90ml
— 80ml
— 70ml
— 60ml
— 50ml
— 40ml
— 30ml
— 20ml
— 10ml

crystals in. See how they dissolve? Watch the weird purple smoke rise from the beaker. Neat, huh?

This is just one of thousands of experiments you can try with my Denzil Dexter home science kit. They are all included in my book, *Science the easy way*. If you want a copy send some dough to me, at the Astro-science Department, University Of Southern California, Santa Cruz, California. (You can also send away for my other book, 'Space Bats – Shocking evidence of a Government cover up.')

Good luck and may the force be with you.

THE ADVENTURES OF UNLUCKY ALF

ISLE·of MAN

Come to the Isle Of Man.

When Robert Louis Stevenson wrote Treasure Island, perhaps the Isle of Man was not so far from his thoughts, because, you see, the Isle Of Man is an *island* with many *treasures*... But then again, maybe he wasn't thinking of us, since his book is set on a tropical *desert* island covered in palm trees and, well obviously the Isle Of Man's nothing like that.

But anyway, come to the Isle Of Man! with its golden beaches, commanding castles, stunning scenery, marvellous museums, mighty monuments, sunny smiles, and dearth of deviants. Yes, we proudly boast that there are no deviants of any kind on the island, known to the Vikings as Ellan Vannin, or 'Land without deviation.'

Come to the Isle Of Man

At the very heart of the British Isles, yet an independent kingdom in its own right. The island has its own parliament and government, which makes its own laws, such as the punishment (by flogging, death and then more flogging) of homosexuals. Can you think of anything better?

Come to the Isle Of Man, for 227 square miles of beautiful unspoilt landscape, including the island's highest mountain, Snaefell. Climb to the

Below: Peaceful countryside near Ballasalla. Not a deviant in sight. Opposite top: Douglas. Just imagine – no litter, no beggars, no tramps, no homos, nothing. Opposite below: The splendid public toilets in Castletown. Just think, you can use these toilets in peace, in the full knowledge that you won't be fisted by some moustachioed Soho deviant.

top of its 2,036 foot peak and see no deviants for miles around, except on clear days when you can see over to England which is literally crawling with the bastards.

Come to the Isle Of Man

Come to the Isle Of Man, not just for the lovely scenery but also for the entertainment, such as the Yn Chruinnaght Inter Celtic festival where you can watch traditional Manx ceremonies such as flogging the unfaithful wives, punching the children who play with themselves and the public humiliation and execution of homosexuals, or 'Bum Boys' as they are called in the colourful local dialect.

Or come see the plays in the lovely Victorian 'Gaiety Theatre' – though, of course, that doesn't mean gay in the modern way, we mean it in the proper old-fashioned sense of happiness and fun, before those deviant bastards got hold of a beautiful word and twisted it out of shape for their own sick ends. Which means – no Oscar Wilde, Joe Orton or Alan Bennet, but plenty of Shakespeare and the Black &White Minstrels.

Come to the Isle Of Man

Why not visit the Cregneach Village Museum of Deviation, where there are scenes depicting deviants being tortured and killed throughout the ages. Or, of course, there is Tynwald day when we celebrate our unique Manx parliament, the oldest continuous parliament in the world, established by the vikings 1000 years ago, and still preserving the beliefs and values of those days, in great contrast to the political upheaval and rampant acceptance of deviancy in the rest of this perverted and evil world.

So, come to the Isle of Man, for the holiday of a lifetime, but don't bother to come if you're a deviant of any kind.

Listings continue >>>

Caroline Aherne

John Thomson

Paul
Whitehouse

Charlie
Higson

Simon Day

Mark Williams

Arabella Weir

INTRODUCTION ...

This guide is matched perfectly to the Modular Double Award Specification B (1536) from Edexcel and also closely reflects their excellent scheme of work.

The reduction in HIGHER material means that we can combine both tiers in the same volume for greater flexibility. This HIGHER material is clearly indicated by red boxes.

All the material within a module is condensed into a KEY POINTS page both for a last minute recap and to instill confidence by demonstrating the size of the task.

Our excellent value workbook matches the guide page for page and is available from the address opposite.

HOW TO USE THIS REVISION GUIDE

- This guide contains everything you need to know and nothing more.

- Don't just read it! Revise actively! Test yourself without looking at the text.

- Tick each section and diagram as you revise it, and the appropriate tick box on the contents page. Use the Key Points pages only for your final run through.

> HIGHER TIER
> Only revise the 'red boxes' if you are doing Higher Tier. (Ask your teacher about this.)

- And don't forget! You'll need this guide toward the end of year II for your terminal exams.

SOME IMPORTANT FACTS ABOUT YOUR EXAMINATION ...

Your course lasts two years, during which time you will study modules 1-6 from VOLUME 1 plus modules 7-12 in this guide.

Each module test covers both Higher and Foundation Tiers and you are expected to answer 24 multiple choice questions in 20 minutes (less difficult than it sounds!)

All your modular tests together contribute a maximum of 30% towards your final exam mark, so it's well worth taking them seriously.

The first Terminal Exam will cover modules 1-6 and will last 90 minutes. The second Terminal Exam covers modules 7-12 and also lasts 90 minutes. Your Terminal Exam contributes a maximum of 50% of your total marks.

The remaining 20% of available marks is for your coursework.

• CONTENTS

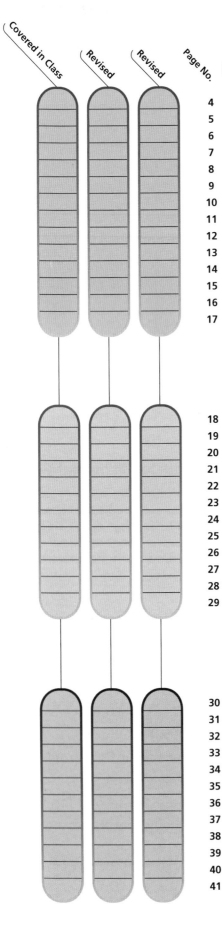

Covered in Class | Revised | Revised | Page No.

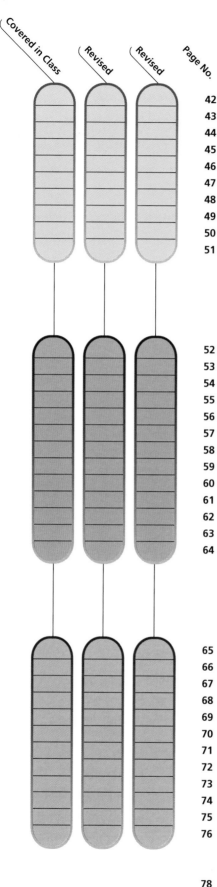

Plant Cell Structure

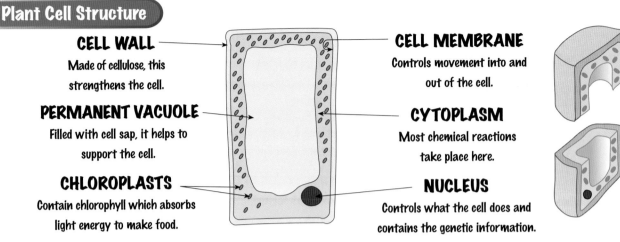

CELL WALL
Made of cellulose, this
strengthens the cell.

CELL MEMBRANE
Controls movement into and
out of the cell.

PERMANENT VACUOLE
Filled with cell sap, it helps to
support the cell.

CYTOPLASM
Most chemical reactions
take place here.

CHLOROPLASTS
Contain chlorophyll which absorbs
light energy to make food.

NUCLEUS
Controls what the cell does and
contains the genetic information.

Most cells are made up mainly of water containing dissolved substances in which chemical reactions are constantly occurring. These reactions are controlled by ENZYMES.

Comparing Plant And Animal Cells

PLANT CELLS	FEATURE	ANIMAL CELLS
YES	NUCLEUS	YES
YES	CYTOPLASM	YES
YES	CELL MEMBRANE	YES
YES	CELL WALL	NO
ALMOST ALWAYS	VACUOLE	NO
THOSE WHICH ARE EXPOSED TO LIGHT	CHLOROPLASTS	NO

Types Of Plant Cell

Some plant cells are highly SPECIALISED to do a particular job ...

ROOT HAIR CELL
Thin hair-like projections give a
big surface area for efficient
absorption of water and minerals.

PALISADE CELL
Column-shaped cells on upper
surface of leaf. Packed with
chloroplasts for photosynthesis.

XYLEM
Long cylinder-like <u>dead</u> cells
for transporting water
through the stem and root.

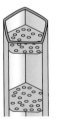

PHLOEM
Long cylinder-like <u>living</u> cells
which transport sugars, made
during photosynthesis, from the
leaves to the fruits and other
storage organs.

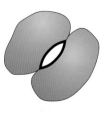

GUARD CELLS
Specialised for regulating
water loss from the leaf
by opening or closing.

Making Food Using Energy From The Sun

Green plants don't absorb food from the soil. They make their own, using sunlight. This is called PHOTOSYNTHESIS, which actually means 'making through light'. It occurs in the cells of green plants, which are exposed to light.

FOUR THINGS ARE NEEDED ...   ... AND TWO THINGS ARE PRODUCED ...

LIGHT
from the sun

CARBON DIOXIDE
diffuses from the air

WATER
from the soil

CHLOROPHYLL
in the leaves

GLUCOSE
for biomass and energy

OXYGEN
released to the atmosphere

The Word Equation For Photosynthesis

$$\text{CARBON DIOXIDE} + \text{WATER} \xrightarrow[\text{CHLOROPHYLL}]{\text{LIGHT}} \text{GLUCOSE} + \text{OXYGEN}$$

How Plants Use This Glucose

1 <u>CONVERSION OF GLUCOSE INTO ENERGY.</u> The plant oxidises some of the glucose to release energy during respiration.

$$\text{GLUCOSE} + \text{OXYGEN} \longrightarrow \text{CARBON DIOXIDE} + \text{WATER} + \text{ENERGY}$$

Some of this energy can then be used to convert other glucose molecules into larger molecules needed by the cell eg. **2** to **4** below.

2 <u>CONVERSION OF GLUCOSE INTO STARCH.</u> The plant does this because starch is an insoluble carbohydrate and therefore can be stored in cells without causing large amounts of water to accumulate as a result of OSMOSIS.

INDIVIDUAL GLUCOSE MOLECULES.   HUGE, LONG CHAINS OF IDENTICAL GLUCOSE MOLECULES (STARCH).

3 <u>CONVERSION OF GLUCOSE INTO CELLULOSE.</u> Cellulose is needed by the plant for cell walls. It is very similar to the structure of starch, but the long chains are cross-linked to form a meshwork. (You don't need to know the structure for your exam).

INDIVIDUAL GLUCOSE MOLECULES.   LONG CROSS-LINKED CHAINS OF GLUCOSE MOLECULES (CELLULOSE).

4 <u>CONVERSION OF GLUCOSE, NITRATES AND OTHER NUTRIENTS INTO PROTEINS.</u> The plant needs protein for growth and also to make enzymes.

INDIVIDUAL GLUCOSE MOLECULES   **+ NITRATES**   lots of **AMINO ACIDS**   **PROTEINS**

LONG CHAINS OF DIFFERENT AMINO ACIDS.

Measuring The Rate Of Photosynthesis

Since we can't see photosynthesis happening we have to observe it indirectly by measuring the production of oxygen in an aquatic plant. Canadian pondweed (Elodea) is ideal for this and can be used in the apparatus shown. Light intensity can be varied by changing the voltage across the lamp, temperature can be varied by using a thermostatic heater, and carbon dioxide concentration can be varied by adding different volumes of sodium hydrogencarbonate solution. The rate can be measured by counting bubbles or measuring volume produced over a fixed time.

Factors Affecting Photosynthesis

In practice, TEMPERATURE, CARBON DIOXIDE CONCENTRATION and LIGHT INTENSITY can interact to limit the rate of photosynthesis. Any one of them, at a particular time, may be the limiting factor.

EFFECT OF TEMPERATURE

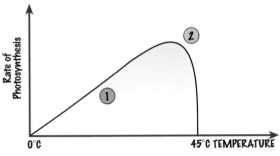

(1) As the temperature rises so does the rate of photosynthesis. This means temperature is limiting the rate of photosynthesis.

(2) As the temperature approaches 45°C the enzymes controlling photosynthesis start to be destroyed and the rate of photosynthesis eventually declines to zero.

EFFECT OF CARBON DIOXIDE CONCENTRATION

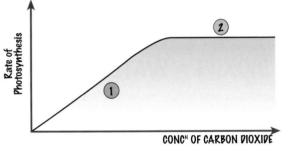

(1) As the carbon dioxide concentration rises so does the rate of photosynthesis. This means carbon dioxide is limiting the rate of photosynthesis.

(2) Rise in carbon dioxide now has no effect. Carbon dioxide is no longer the limiting factor. This means SUNLIGHT or TEMPERATURE must be the limiting factor.

EFFECT OF LIGHT INTENSITY

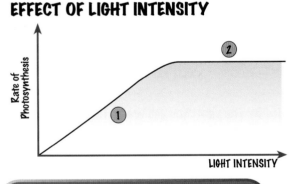

(1) As the light intensity increases so does the rate of photosynthesis. This means light intensity is limiting the rate of photosynthesis.

(2) Rise in light intensity now has no effect. Light intensity is no longer the limiting factor.
This means CARBON DIOXIDE or TEMPERATURE must be the limiting factor.

Plant Mineral Requirements

For healthy growth plants need mineral ions which they absorb through their roots ...

NITRATES
- Needed to make proteins ...
- ... if there's a shortage, it leads to ...
- ... STUNTED GROWTH and YELLOW OLDER LEAVES.

MAGNESIUM
- Needed to make chlorophyll for photosynthesis ...
- ... if there's a shortage, it leads to ...
- ... YELLOWING OF LEAF MARGINS.

Osmosis

OSMOSIS is ... the **DIFFUSION OF WATER** ...

... from a **DILUTE SOLUTION** ...

... to a **MORE CONCENTRATED SOLUTION** ...

... through a **SELECTIVELY PERMEABLE MEMBRANE** that ...

... **ALLOWS THE PASSAGE OF WATER MOLECULES BUT NOT SOLUTE MOLECULES.**

MEMBRANE

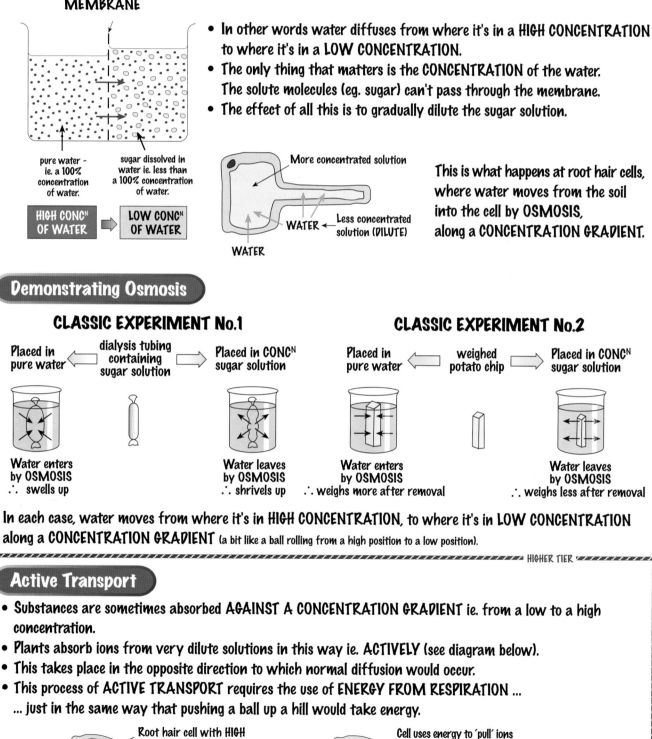

pure water -
ie. a 100%
concentration
of water.

sugar dissolved in
water ie. less than
a 100% concentration
of water.

HIGH CONCⁿ OF WATER ➡ **LOW CONCⁿ OF WATER**

- In other words water diffuses from where it's in a HIGH CONCENTRATION to where it's in a LOW CONCENTRATION.
- The only thing that matters is the CONCENTRATION of the water. The solute molecules (eg. sugar) can't pass through the membrane.
- The effect of all this is to gradually dilute the sugar solution.

More concentrated solution

WATER ← Less concentrated solution (DILUTE)

WATER

This is what happens at root hair cells, where water moves from the soil into the cell by OSMOSIS, along a CONCENTRATION GRADIENT.

Demonstrating Osmosis

CLASSIC EXPERIMENT No.1

Placed in pure water ⬅ dialysis tubing containing sugar solution ➡ Placed in CONCⁿ sugar solution

Water enters by OSMOSIS ∴ swells up

Water leaves by OSMOSIS ∴ shrivels up

CLASSIC EXPERIMENT No.2

Placed in pure water ⬅ weighed potato chip ➡ Placed in CONCⁿ sugar solution

Water enters by OSMOSIS ∴ weighs more after removal

Water leaves by OSMOSIS ∴ weighs less after removal

In each case, water moves from where it's in HIGH CONCENTRATION, to where it's in LOW CONCENTRATION along a CONCENTRATION GRADIENT (a bit like a ball rolling from a high position to a low position).

— HIGHER TIER —

Active Transport

- Substances are sometimes absorbed AGAINST A CONCENTRATION GRADIENT ie. from a low to a high concentration.
- Plants absorb ions from very dilute solutions in this way ie. ACTIVELY (see diagram below).
- This takes place in the opposite direction to which normal diffusion would occur.
- This process of ACTIVE TRANSPORT requires the use of ENERGY FROM RESPIRATION ...

... just in the same way that pushing a ball up a hill would take energy.

Root hair cell with HIGH CONCⁿ of NITRATE IONS.

Soil with LOW CONCⁿ of NITRATE IONS.

Cell uses energy to 'pull' ions against the concentration gradient.

NITRATE IONS

The Leaf

Leaves are BROAD, THIN and FLAT with lots of INTERNAL AIR SPACES in order to make them efficient at photosynthesis by providing a large surface area. They also have STOMATA on their undersurface to allow CARBON DIOXIDE in and OXYGEN out. This however leads to loss of water vapour in a process called TRANSPIRATION.

THIS IS A CROSS-SECTION OF A LEAF.

STOMATA

H_2O CO_2 CO_2 H_2O

- This WAXY LAYER stops too much water from just evaporating away from the leaf.
- Transpiration is more rapid in HOT, DRY or WINDY conditions.
- Water lost by transpiration must be replaced by water from the soil.

The Stem

Flowering plants have separate transport systems for water and nutrients...
- **PHLOEM TISSUE** ... transports sugars, made during photosynthesis, from the leaves to the rest of the plant, including storage organs eg. fruits and tubers and growing regions.
- **XYLEM TISSUE** ... transports water and soluble mineral salts from the roots to the stem and leaves, to replace the water lost in transpiration and photosynthesis.

1. Water EVAPORATES from the internal leaf cells through the STOMATA.

2. Water passes from the XYLEM vessels to leaf cells due to OSMOSIS ...

3. ... which 'pulls' the entire 'thread' of water in that vessel upwards by a very small amount.

4. Water enters XYLEM from root tissue to replace water which has moved upwards.

5. Water enters ROOT HAIR CELLS by OSMOSIS to replace water which has entered the XYLEM.

CROSS-SECTION THROUGH A STEM

XYLEM   PHLOEM

PHLOEM

SUGARS

LIVING CELLS WHICH TRANSPORT SUGARS

SOLUBLE MINERAL SALTS + WATER

XYLEM

DEAD CELLS WHICH TRANSPORT WATER

The transpiration stream is powered by evaporation of water from the leaf.

The Root

WATER enters the plant via the roots.
Most of it is absorbed by the ROOT HAIR CELLS by osmosis. This water passes into the xylem vessels to replace water which is continually moving up the stem.
The surface area of the roots is increased by the presence of root hairs. This increases the rate at which they can absorb water and minerals and is another typical example of how exchange surfaces are adapted to their function.

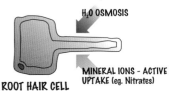

H_2O OSMOSIS

MINERAL IONS - ACTIVE UPTAKE (eg. Nitrates)

ROOT HAIR CELL

Controlling Water Loss

Water is a vital commodity for all plants since it is needed for photosynthesis, for support and also as the main constituent of cytoplasm.

However carbon dioxide and oxygen need to be able to enter and leave the leaf, and they do so via diffusion through the stomata ...

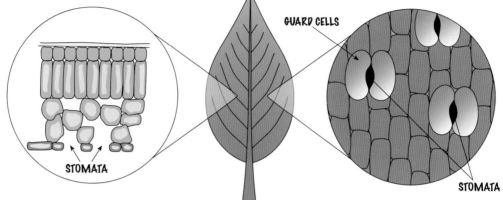

GUARD CELLS

STOMATA

STOMATA

• Unfortunately, WATER VAPOUR, from the moist surfaces of the leaf cells, also diffuses out of the stomata.
• WATER LOSS THROUGH TRANSPIRATION IS THE 'PRICE THE PLANT MUST PAY' IN ORDER TO PHOTOSYNTHESISE. However ...
• The size of the stomata is controlled by a pair of GUARD CELLS.
• If plants lose water faster than it is taken up by the roots ...
    ... the stomata can close to prevent wilting and eventual dehydration.

The rate of water loss from the leaves (transpiration rate) can be measured using a simple POTOMETER, and is heavily influenced by ...
• the temperature ... (increases with warmth)
• the humidity ... (decreases with higher humidity)
• the moment of air ... (increases with wind)
• the light intensity ... (increases with brightness)

A SIMPLE POTOMETER

Water evaporating

Bubble moves along as the water moves to the leaves

Plastic tubing

Maintaining Support

When the plant has plenty of water, the cell contents 'swell up' and press against the cell wall. This increases the rigidity of the plant tissue and provides the main method of support in young, non-woody stems.

Plenty of water in soil

The reasons for this are as follows ...

• If a cell is in a less concentrated solution, water enters it by osmosis, and causes the cell contents to press up against the cell wall.
    This maintains the TURGIDITY of the cell - a bit like a balloon inside a cereal box!

Insufficient water

• If a cell is in a less concentrated solution, water leaves the cell and eventually the cell contents dehydrate to such an extent that they pull away from the cell wall.
    Turgidity is therefore lost and the plant may wilt.
    We refer to the cell as now being FLACCID.

H_2O

TURGID CELL

H_2O

FLACCID CELL

Plant Responses

Plants are sensitive to: • **LIGHT**   • **MOISTURE**   • **GRAVITY**
• SHOOTS grow TOWARDS LIGHT and AGAINST THE FORCE OF GRAVITY.
• ROOTS grow TOWARDS MOISTURE and in the DIRECTION OF GRAVITY.
These responses are controlled by HORMONES which coordinate and control growth.
Hormones are produced in the growing tips of shoots and roots but can then collect unevenly ...
... causing unequal growth rates in different parts of the plant.

Gravity

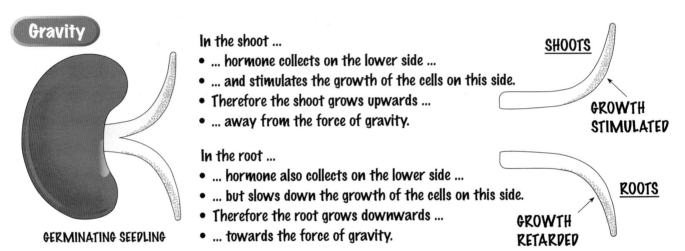

GERMINATING SEEDLING

In the shoot ...
• ... hormone collects on the lower side ...
• ... and stimulates the growth of the cells on this side.
• Therefore the shoot grows upwards ...
• ... away from the force of gravity.

In the root ...
• ... hormone also collects on the lower side ...
• ... but slows down the growth of the cells on this side.
• Therefore the root grows downwards ...
• ... towards the force of gravity.

SHOOTS

GROWTH STIMULATED

ROOTS

GROWTH RETARDED

The key thing to remember here is that the hormone produced in the growing tips has the OPPOSITE EFFECT in roots and shoots.
• The hormone Ⓢ TIMULATES cell growth in Ⓢ HOOTS, and ...
• ... Ⓡ ETARDS cell growth in Ⓡ OOTS.

Light

• In shoots, LIGHT causes HORMONES ...
    • ... to accumulate on the shaded part of the stem ...
        • ... which causes growth on that side ...
            • ... and the plant grows towards the sun.

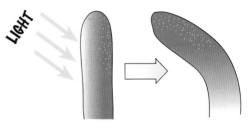

LIGHT

Commercial Use Of Plant Hormones

• ROOTING COMPOUND - Consists of a hormone which encourages ...
                ... the GROWTH OF ROOTS ...
                    ... in STEM CUTTINGS ...
                        ... so lots of plants can be obtained from only one

• TISSUE CULTURE - A few cells are scraped off into several beakers ...
        ... containing nutrients and hormones.
            ... Lots of genetically identical plants are produced.

• RIPENING HORMONE - Causes plants to ripen at set time ...
            ... sometimes during transport.
                Achieved by spraying.

• SELECTIVE WEEDKILLERS - Disrupt the normal growth patterns ...
                ... of their target plants ...
                    ... leaving other plants untouched.

Food Chains

FOOD CHAINS show which organism is eating which other organism.
They also show the TRANSFER OF ENERGY and MATERIALS from organism to organism.
- ENERGY from the SUN enters the FOOD CHAIN when green plants ABSORB SUNLIGHT in order to PHOTOSYNTHESISE.
- FEEDING passes this ENERGY from one organism to the next ALONG THE FOOD CHAIN.

LETTUCE
All food chains start with a green plant called the PRODUCER.

RABBIT
The RABBIT is a HERBIVORE (plant eater) and the PRIMARY CONSUMER.

STOAT
The STOAT is a CARNIVORE (meat eater) and the SECONDARY CONSUMER.

FOX
The FOX is the TOP CARNIVORE and the TERTIARY CONSUMER.

The ARROWS show THE FLOW OF ENERGY and BIOMASS (living material) along the foodchain

Transfer Of Energy And Biomass

- Some of the energy and biomass is incorporated into the consumer's body.
- However biomass and energy are lost at every stage of a food chain because ...
- ... materials and energy are lost in an organism's <u>faeces (waste)</u>, and ...
- ... energy is 'lost' as <u>movement energy</u> and <u>'waste' heat energy</u> originally provided by respiration.
- This last statement is particularly true of warm-blooded animals (birds and mammals).
- Consequently, only a tiny proportion of the available energy is transferred to the next feeding level.

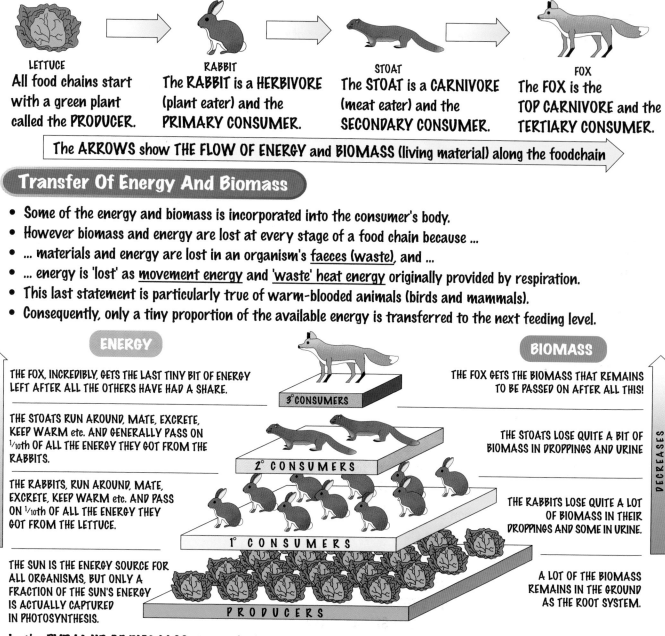

ENERGY

THE FOX, INCREDIBLY, GETS THE LAST TINY BIT OF ENERGY LEFT AFTER ALL THE OTHERS HAVE HAD A SHARE.

THE STOATS RUN AROUND, MATE, EXCRETE, KEEP WARM etc. AND GENERALLY PASS ON 1/10th OF ALL THE ENERGY THEY GOT FROM THE RABBITS.

THE RABBITS, RUN AROUND, MATE, EXCRETE, KEEP WARM etc. AND PASS ON 1/10th OF ALL THE ENERGY THEY GOT FROM THE LETTUCE.

THE SUN IS THE ENERGY SOURCE FOR ALL ORGANISMS, BUT ONLY A FRACTION OF THE SUN'S ENERGY IS ACTUALLY CAPTURED IN PHOTOSYNTHESIS.

BIOMASS

THE FOX GETS THE BIOMASS THAT REMAINS TO BE PASSED ON AFTER ALL THIS!

THE STOATS LOSE QUITE A BIT OF BIOMASS IN DROPPINGS AND URINE

THE RABBITS LOSE QUITE A LOT OF BIOMASS IN THEIR DROPPINGS AND SOME IN URINE.

A LOT OF THE BIOMASS REMAINS IN THE GROUND AS THE ROOT SYSTEM.

DECREASES

3° CONSUMERS
2° CONSUMERS
1° CONSUMERS
PRODUCERS

In the PYRAMID OF BIOMASS above, the loss of energy and biomass is indicated and explains why such a representation of a food chain must always be 'pyramid-shaped'.

Efficiency Of Energy Transfer In Food Chains Involving Mammals

Mammals use a lot of energy from respiration just to maintain body temperature. This loss of thermal energy to a cooler environment means that food chains involving mammals are very inefficient at transferring energy from one feeding level to the next. This has implications in food production.

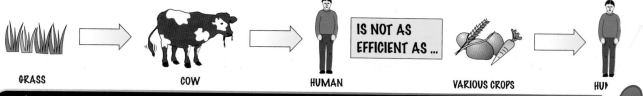

GRASS   COW   HUMAN

IS NOT AS EFFICIENT AS ...

VARIOUS CROPS   HU

Decay

Decaying is a process involving the BREAKDOWN of complex substances into simpler ones. It requires ...

• MICROORGANISMS   • WARM TEMPERATURES   • MOISTURE   • OXYGEN

The Carbon Cycle

In a stable community, the processes which remove materials ...

... are balanced by processes which return materials. A sort of constant recycling.

The constant recycling of carbon is called the Carbon Cycle.

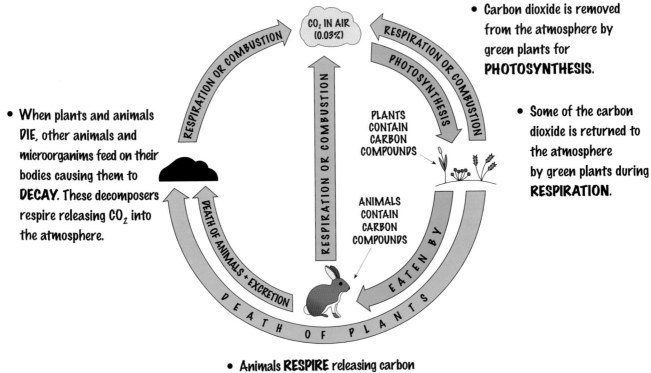

• When plants and animals DIE, other animals and microorganims feed on their bodies causing them to **DECAY**. These decomposers respire releasing CO_2 into the atmosphere.

• Carbon dioxide is removed from the atmosphere by green plants for **PHOTOSYNTHESIS**.

• Some of the carbon dioxide is returned to the atmosphere by green plants during **RESPIRATION**.

• Animals **RESPIRE** releasing carbon dioxide into the atmosphere.

The FOUR MAIN PROCESSES in the cycle are:

• RESPIRATION - <u>releases</u> carbon dioxide into the air.
• PHOTOSYNTHESIS - <u>removes</u> carbon dioxide from the air.
• DECAY - of <u>plants</u>, <u>animals</u> and <u>faeces</u> (waste material from the process of digestion) returns CO_2 to the air.
• COMBUSTION - of any organic material <u>returns</u> carbon dioxide to the atmosphere.

Maintaining The Balance

Plants respire all the time, as do animals. However during daylight hours plants also photosynthesise. Happily for us, the amount of oxygen they use for respiration is only a tiny fraction of the amount they produce during photosynthesis. This means that the oxygen consumed by animals is more than adequately replaced by photosynthesis, in normal circumstances. However, the levels of oxygen and carbon dioxide in the atmosphere depend upon the fine balance between respiration and photosynthesis being maintained. The burning of fossil fuels is perhaps starting to upset the balance.

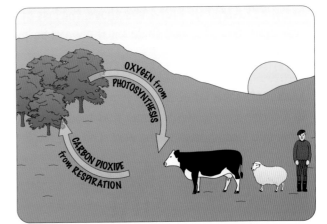

- The NITROGEN CYCLE shows how NITROGEN and its COMPOUNDS are ...
  ... RECYCLED in nature.
- NITROGEN is a vital element of all LIVING THINGS ...
  ... and is used in the PRODUCTION OF PROTEINS.
- PROTEINS are used in PLANT and ANIMAL GROWTH.

The Nitrogen Cycle

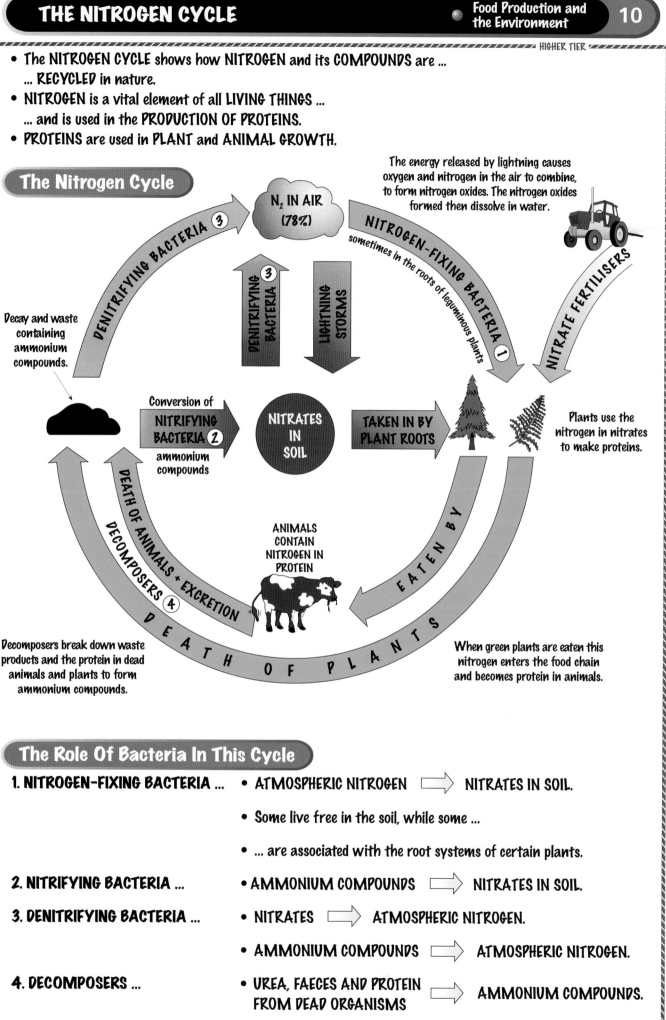

The energy released by lightning causes oxygen and nitrogen in the air to combine, to form nitrogen oxides. The nitrogen oxides formed then dissolve in water.

N_2 IN AIR (78%)

DENITRIFYING BACTERIA ③

NITROGEN-FIXING BACTERIA ①
sometimes in the roots of leguminous plants

NITRATE FERTILISERS

DENITRIFYING BACTERIA ③

LIGHTNING STORMS

Decay and waste containing ammonium compounds.

Conversion of NITRIFYING BACTERIA ② ammonium compounds

NITRATES IN SOIL

TAKEN IN BY PLANT ROOTS

Plants use the nitrogen in nitrates to make proteins.

DEATH OF ANIMALS + EXCRETION

DECOMPOSERS ④

DEATH OF PLANTS

EATEN BY

ANIMALS CONTAIN NITROGEN IN PROTEIN

Decomposers break down waste products and the protein in dead animals and plants to form ammonium compounds.

When green plants are eaten this nitrogen enters the food chain and becomes protein in animals.

The Role Of Bacteria In This Cycle

1. NITROGEN-FIXING BACTERIA ...
- ATMOSPHERIC NITROGEN ⟹ NITRATES IN SOIL.
- Some live free in the soil, while some ...
- ... are associated with the root systems of certain plants.

2. NITRIFYING BACTERIA ...
- AMMONIUM COMPOUNDS ⟹ NITRATES IN SOIL.

3. DENITRIFYING BACTERIA ...
- NITRATES ⟹ ATMOSPHERIC NITROGEN.
- AMMONIUM COMPOUNDS ⟹ ATMOSPHERIC NITROGEN.

4. DECOMPOSERS ...
- UREA, FAECES AND PROTEIN FROM DEAD ORGANISMS ⟹ AMMONIUM COMPOUNDS.

Deforestation

Deforestation, as the name suggests, means the large scale removal of forested areas. This has happened, most often in recent years, in tropical and sub-tropical areas. It has happened mainly for the following reasons...
- To provide fuel for people living in that particular region.
- To provide land for agricultural use.
- To provide space for building urban developments.

This of course has had an environmental effect which has contributed to an increase in the level of carbon dioxide in the atmosphere. This is due to two factors, ...
- Combustion (and decomposition) of the felled trees produces carbon dioxide directly.
- Reduced numbers of trees means a reduction in the level of photosynthesis which means less carbon dioxide is removed from the atmosphere.

Sustainable Forestry

Sustainable resources are resources that can be maintained in the long-term at a level that allows appropriate consumption by people.

Scandinavian countries use a lot of pine wood to make furniture, paper and to provide energy. To ensure the long term economic viability of pine-related industries, and to avoid environmental damage, companies restock the pine forests by planting a new sapling for each mature tree they cut down.

Use Of Pesticides

Crops can be damaged by herbivorous insects, competing weeds and fungal infections, and consequently farmers are often keen to use INSECTICIDES, HERBICIDES and FUNGICIDES to reduce the damage. There are however environmental implications ....

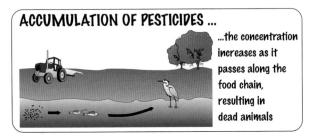

ACCUMULATION OF PESTICIDES ...

...the concentration increases as it passes along the food chain, resulting in dead animals

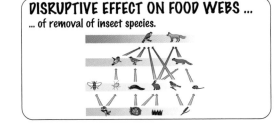

DISRUPTIVE EFFECT ON FOOD WEBS ...
... of removal of insect species.

Biological Control Of Pests

Instead of using pesticides, natural predators can be used against the pests eg. ...

1 ... the COTTONY CUSHION SCALE INSECT was a pest that ATTACKED CITRUS FRUIT CROPS ...
   ... but the farmers introduced the LADYBIRD BEETLE and the pest's numbers were significantly reduced.

2 ... the PRICKLY PEAR CACTUS was growing at a fantastic rate and taking over a lot of useful farm land ...
   ... so a MOTH, that had larvae that fed on the cactus' tissues, was introduced and the problem was solved.

ALSO, STERILE MALES can be introduced into the environment, and these compete with the existing males for mates. However if they succeed in getting one they can't produce any offspring and so the population declines naturally.

ADVANTAGES OF BIOLOGICAL PEST CONTROL	ADVANTAGES OF CHEMICAL PEST CONTROL
• The predator only attacks the pest (species specific). • Once introduced it can have an impact over many years. • The pest does not become resistant to the predator.	• It is generally cheaper than biological control. • It removes a greater number of pests more quickly. • It is usually easier to administer.

Greenhouse Management

The essential aim in greenhouse management of food production is to be able to control all the possible variables which could influence crop yield. In an open environment this is, of course, impossible. However, under glass many of the variables can be controlled ...

- INTERNAL LIGHTING can be used to supplement the natural light on a dull day, or to artificially increase the day-length. This increases photosynthetic activity.
- EXTRA HEATING can be used to provide the optimum temperature for photosynthesis, even during the winter months.
- ADDITIONAL CARBON DIOXIDE can be pumped into the greenhouse to provide extra raw material for photosynthesis.
- PRECISE AMOUNTS OF FERTILISER can be administrered to the crop via the water supply which can also be adjusted to meet the plants' needs.
- PRECISE AMOUNTS OF PESTICIDES can also be applied without fear of much of it being wind blown away from the target crop.
- BIOLOGICAL PEST CONTROL can also be more accurately introduced and more carefully monitored under glass.

The greenhouses used in this type of food production are not the sort which are found at the bottom of domestic gardens! They are vast affairs covering several acres of land and demand skilled management techniques in order to run smoothly.

Costs And Benefits Of Intensive Farming

Intensive farming incurs more costs but produces a greater yield from the area being cultivated. The proportionally greater increase in yield leads to greater profits.

PROFIT AND LOSS ACCOUNT
INTENSIVE FARMING

OCTOBER

COSTS	
ELECTRICITY BILL	2016.76
CALOR GAS BOTTLES	790.10
CARBON DIOXIDE CYLINDERS	321.46
FERTILISERS (INORGANIC)	1200.00
PESTICIDES	280.50
OTHERS	116.48
TOTAL	£4725.30
REVENUE	
SALE OF CROP	9123.50
NET PROFIT	£4398.20

(GREATER COSTS)
(MUCH GREATER YIELD)
(HIGHER PROFIT)

PROFIT AND LOSS ACCOUNT
'NORMAL' FARMING

OCTOBER

COSTS	
ELECTRICITY BILL	76.20
FERTILISERS (ORGANIC)	800.00
PESTICIDES	520.80
OTHERS	134.12
TOTAL	£1531.12
REVENUE	
SALE OF CROP	4581.37
NET PROFIT	£3050.25

(LOWER COSTS)
(LOWER YIELD)
(SMALLER PROFIT)

However, there is an environmental cost, since non-renewable resources such as fossil fuels must be used to generate electricity and may also have been used in the production of CO_2, fertilisers, pesticides and the construction of the greenhouses.

Distribution And Relative Abundance

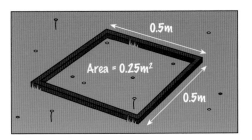

- Quadrats consist of 4 pieces of metal linked rigidly to form a square. These are used for estimating plant populations. They will provide excellent results as long as the quadrats are thrown randomly. A system must be worked out beforehand and stuck to rigidly. The population of a certain species of plant can then be estimated. eg. imagine an AVERAGE of 4 dandelion plants are found in each 0.25m² (quadrat). A scientist would estimate 16 dandelion plants are found in each 1m² and 16,000 dandelion plants in a field if it is 1000m².

- They can also be used to work out percentage cover. In this instance, after each throw of the quadrat, the percentage cover of each plant would be noted down. This of course is only an approximation but nevertheless if sufficient quadrats are thrown a good indication of the plant cover in a particular area can be gained.

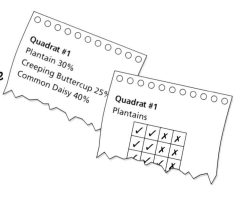

- Partitioned quadrats can also be used to give a 'presence' or 'absence' score. In this case fine nylon cord is used to divide the quadrat into a number of sections and ticks or crosses are used to indicate the presence or absence of a particular species of plant.

Improving Biodiversity

Biodiversity refers to the number of different types of living things in an ecosystem. In the absence of artificial ecosystems created by humans, the diversity of life in every habitat on the planet would be enormous. However, the creation of huge fields containing one crop, the deforestation of vast areas and ridiculous overfishing are threatening biodiversity.

- In the mid-1970's fish stocks in the North Sea dwindled due to OVERFISHING. Nations proposed various measures to remedy the situation including imposing fishing quotas to limit the catch a vessel was allowed to land over a certain period of time.

- Amongst other proposals implemented was limiting the mesh size of nets so that younger fish weren't caught before they reached breeding age. This degree of conservation is necessary to maintain the biodiversity of the seas.

Endangered Species

- When COUNTRIES or COMPANIES neglect the ideas of sustainable development ...
  ... various species can become endangered.

- The RED KITE was exploited ...
  ... for its feathers.

- The OSPREY numbers reduced ...
  ... as its habitats were destroyed

- The RED SQUIRREL was endangered ...
  ... with the introduction of the grey squirrel.

- Many ENDANGERED SPECIES are now PROTECTED ...
  ... the COUNTRYSIDE COUNCIL FOR WALES provides LEGAL PROTECTION for red squirrels who cannot be trapped, killed or kept except under special licence ...
  ... the red kite and osprey both have PROTECTED SITES in Wales where they can live and breed undisturbed.

- EDUCATION has become a powerful 'weapon' in ...
  ... protecting endangered species and promoting the ideas behind sustainable development.

PLANT CELLS AND OSMOSIS

	PLANT CELLS	FEATURE	ANIMAL CELLS
CELL WALL	YES	NUCLEUS	YES
CELL MEMBRANE	YES	CYTOPLASM	YES
PERMANENT VACUOLE	YES	CELL MEMBRANE	YES
CYTOPLASM	YES	CELL WALL	NO
CHLOROPLASTS	ALMOST ALWAYS	VACUOLE	NO
NUCLEUS	THOSE WHICH ARE EXPOSED TO LIGHT	CHLOROPLASTS	NO

ROOT HAIR CELL   **GUARD CELLS**   **PHLOEM**   **PALISADE CELL**   **XYLEM**

'OSMOSIS is the diffusion of water from a dilute solution to a more concentrated solution through a selectively permeable membrane that allows the passage of water molecules but not solute molecules'

PURE H_2O SUGAR + H_2O

• Remember the two classic experiments with dialysis tubing and 'chips'.

| HIGH CONC^N OF WATER | → | LOW CONC^N OF WATER |

ACTIVE TRANSPORT requires energy to absorb ions against a concentration gradient

PHOTOSYNTHESIS AND PLANT MINERAL REQUIREMENTS

$$\text{CARBON DIOXIDE} + \text{WATER} \xrightarrow[\text{Chlorophyll}]{\text{Light}} \text{GLUCOSE} + \text{OXYGEN}$$

The glucose provides energy via respiration which is used to ...
   CONVERT GLUCOSE INTO STARCH
   CONVERT GLUCOSE INTO CELLULOSE for cell walls
   CONVERT GLUCOSE AND NITRATES INTO AMINO ACIDS for proteins

FACTORS AFFECTING PHOTOSYNTHESIS

TEMPERATURE CO_2 CONCENTRATION *1   LIGHT INTENSITY *2

*1 At this point, sunlight or temperature must be limiting factor.
*2 At this point, carbon dioxide or temperature must be limiting factor.

MINERAL REQUIREMENTS

Lack of NITRATES leads to stunted growth and yellow older leaves.

Lack of MAGNESIUM means the plant can't produce chlorophyll for photosynthesis. Leads to yellowing of leaf margins.

TRANSPIRATION, WATER LOSS AND WILTING

① Evaporation via stomata.
② Water from the xylem to leaf via osmosis ...
③ 'Thread' of water in xylem pulled upwards.
④ Water enters xylem from roots.
⑤ Water enters root hair cells via osmosis to replace water which has entered the xylem.

PHLOEM   XYLEM

SUGARS   SOLUBLE MINERAL SALTS   WATER

LIVING CELLS   DEAD CELLS

'CONTROLLING WATER LOSS ... stomata stay open to allow diffusion of gases in photosynthesis but if there is insufficient water the guard cells become flaccid and the stomata close'.

TURGID   **FLACCID**

H_2O Water passes into the cells by osmosis if they are in a less concentrated solution. H_2O

PLANT HORMONES AND ENERGY TRANSFER IN FOOD CHAINS

HORMONES

In shoots growth is stimulated.

In roots growth is retarded.

LIGHT

Light causes hormones to accumulate on the shaded part of the stem.

Hormones can be used artificially as ROOTING COMPOUNDS, RIPENING HORMONE, SELECTIVE WEEDKILLERS and to stimulate tissue culture.

FOOD CHAINS

All food chains start with a green plant called the PRODUCER.   The RABBIT is a HERBIVORE (plant eater) and the PRIMARY CONSUMER.   The STOAT is a CARNIVORE (meat eater) and the SECONDARY CONSUMER.   The FOX is the TOP CARNIVORE and the TERTIARY CONSUMER.

Biomass and energy are lost at every stage of a food chain through ... FAECES, MOVEMENT and 'WASTE' HEAT ENERGY. The latter is particularly true of mammals and therefore food chains involving them are inefficient at transferring energy.

FLOW OF ENERGY

3° CONSUMERS
2° CONSUMERS
1° CONSUMERS
PRODUCERS

CARBON CYCLE AND NITROGEN CYCLE

DECAY needs ...
• MICROORGANISMS
• WARMTH
• MOISTURE
• OXYGEN.

CARBON CYCLE

CO_2 IN AIR (0.03%)

RESPIRATION   PHOTOSYNTHESIS

DECOMPOSERS

PLANTS CONTAIN CARBON COMPOUNDS

ANIMALS CONTAIN CARBON COMPOUNDS

DEATH • EXCRETION   EATEN

DEATH OF PLANTS

NITROGEN CYCLE

N_2 IN AIR (79%)

DENITRIFYING   NITROGEN-FIXING
LIGHTNING STORMS

Conversion of NITRIFYING ammonium compounds   NITRATES IN SOIL   TAKEN IN BY PLANT ROOTS   FERTILISERS

ANIMALS CONTAIN NITROGEN IN PROTEIN

DEATH • EXCRETION   EATEN BY

DEATH OF PLANTS

1. NITROGEN-FIXING BACTERIA ...
• ATMOSPHERIC NITROGEN ⟹ NITRATES IN SOIL.
• Some live free in the soil, while some ...
• ... are associated with the root systems of certain plants.

2. NITRIFYING BACTERIA ...
• AMMONIUM COMPOUNDS ⟹ NITRATES IN SOIL.

3. DENITRIFYING BACTERIA ...
• NITRATES ⟹ ATMOSPHERIC NITROGEN.
• AMMONIUM COMPOUNDS ⟹ ATMOSPHERIC NITROGEN.

4. DECOMPOSERS ...
• DEAD MATTER + WASTE ⟹ AMMONIUM COMPOUNDS.

MANAGING THE ENVIRONMENT

DEFORESTATION ... for fuel, building and agriculture, affects the environment due to combustion and decomposition of felled trees, and reduced levels of photosynthesis. Sustainable forestry requires a replanting programme.

PESTICIDES ... can accumulate in individuals as they move up the food chain, and can also have a disruptive effect on food webs.

BIOLOGICAL CONTROL ... uses a natural predator to kill pests. Sterile males may also be used. This is species-specific, lasts a long time and the pest does not become resistant. However, it is never entirely eliminated, is only successful in 20% of cases and costs a great deal in terms of time, research and money.

GREENHOUSE MANAGEMENT ... aims to control these variables in order to maximise yield; light intensity; temperature; CO_2 level; nutrient levels; pests. Although efficient, it is very energy intensive.

DISTRIBUTION AND RELATIVE ABUNDANCE ... quadrats are thrown randomly and number of plants as percentage cover can be quite accurately assessed. This can be used to assess BIODIVERSITY ie. how many different types of plants are present. Biodiversity can be helped by conservation measures. eg. ① North Sea cod stocks are protected by fishing quotas and limiting mesh size. ② Pine forests in Scandinavia where a new sapling is planted for every tree cut down.

ENDANGERED SPECIES ... eg. • Red kite for its feathers. • Osprey's habitat destroyed. • Red squirrel out-competed by grey squirrel. There is legal protection, protected sites and education programmes to combat the problem. Sustainable development of forests may help to provide a habitat for various species to live in.

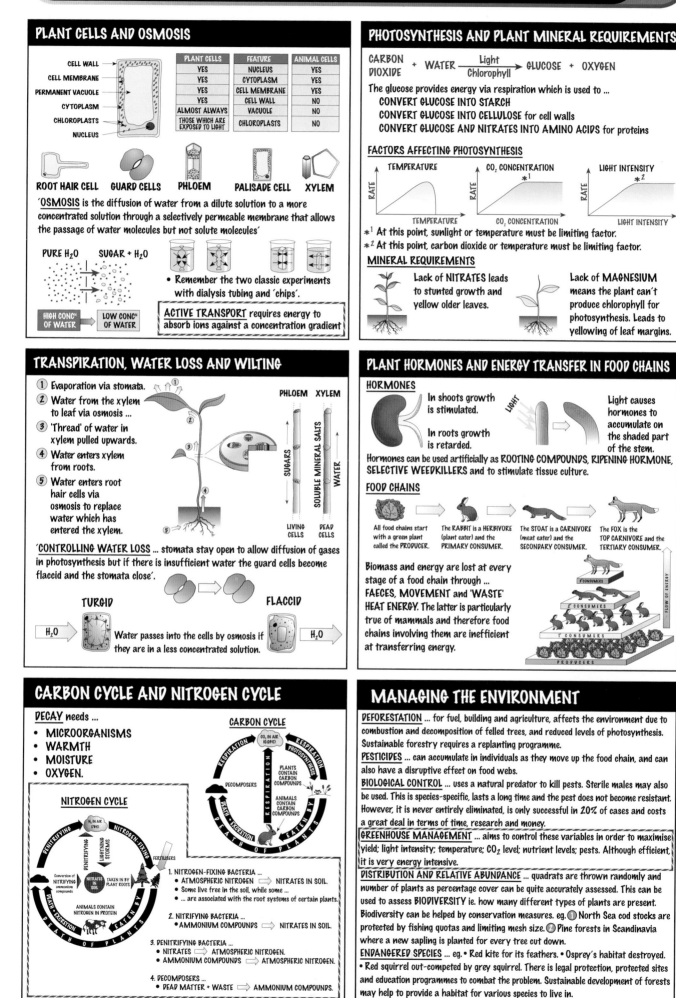

The Breathing System

The most important structures in the breathing system are shown in the diagram below ...

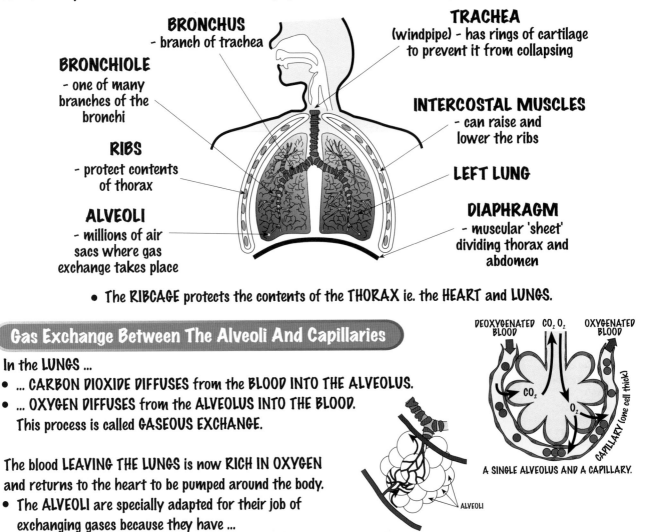

BRONCHUS
- branch of trachea

TRACHEA
(windpipe) - has rings of cartilage to prevent it from collapsing

BRONCHIOLE
- one of many branches of the bronchi

INTERCOSTAL MUSCLES
- can raise and lower the ribs

RIBS
- protect contents of thorax

LEFT LUNG

ALVEOLI
- millions of air sacs where gas exchange takes place

DIAPHRAGM
- muscular 'sheet' dividing thorax and abdomen

- The RIBCAGE protects the contents of the THORAX ie. the HEART and LUNGS.

Gas Exchange Between The Alveoli And Capillaries

In the LUNGS ...
- ... CARBON DIOXIDE DIFFUSES from the BLOOD INTO THE ALVEOLUS.
- ... OXYGEN DIFFUSES from the ALVEOLUS INTO THE BLOOD.
  This process is called GASEOUS EXCHANGE.

DEOXYGENATED BLOOD CO_2 O_2 OXYGENATED BLOOD

CO_2

O_2

CAPILLARY (one cell thick)

A SINGLE ALVEOLUS AND A CAPILLARY.

ALVEOLI

The blood LEAVING THE LUNGS is now RICH IN OXYGEN and returns to the heart to be pumped around the body.
- The ALVEOLI are specially adapted for their job of exchanging gases because they have ...

1 A MASSIVE SURFACE AREA   **2** A MOIST, PERMEABLE SURFACE   **3** AN EXCELLENT BLOOD SUPPLY.

Ventilation

The breathing system is designed to allow oxygen and carbon dioxide to be efficiently exchanged. For this to happen, however, the lungs have to be constantly 'refreshed' by atmospheric air. This happens by increasing and then decreasing the volume of the thorax (chest cavity).

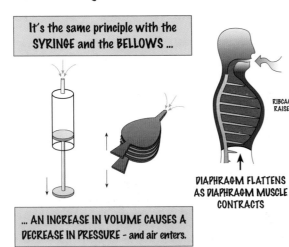

It's the same principle with the SYRINGE and the BELLOWS ...

... AN INCREASE IN VOLUME CAUSES A DECREASE IN PRESSURE - and air enters.

RIBCAGE RAISED

DIAPHRAGM FLATTENS AS DIAPHRAGM MUSCLE CONTRACTS

To inhale:
- The intercostal muscles contract, pulling the ribcage upwards and outwards, like the handle on a bucket.
- At the same time the diaphragm muscles contract causing the diaphragm to flatten.
- These two movements cause an increase in the volume of the thorax ...
- ... and therefore a decrease in pressure which results in atmospheric air entering.

To exhale:
- The intercostal muscles and the diaphragm relax causing the reversal of what happens during inhaling.

Cleaning Up The Air

Specialised cells line all of the respiratory system. Some produce MUCUS, while others have hairs called CILIA which beat the mucus upwards to the mouth. This mucus traps dust and microbes which get pushed out of the lungs and are eventually swallowed. Sometimes when you have a cold you produce too much mucus and have to cough to 'clear your chest'.

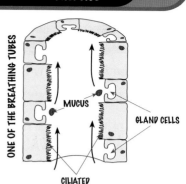

ONE OF THE BREATHING TUBES

MUCUS

GLAND CELLS

CILIATED EPITHELIAL CELLS

The Effects Of Smoking

If the ingredients of cigarette smoke are 'sucked' through cotton wool you will see a brown tarry deposit build up. This smells awful and has a shocking effect on the human body ...

The cilia stop 'beating' because of the tar, causing mucus to build up.

Constant coughing due to build up of mucus damages the air sacs. This is called EMPHYSEMA.

The tar also causes cancer of the lungs, throat, mouth and stomach.

NICOTINE is addictive and narrows blood vessels, increases heart rate and therefore increases blood pressure.

BRONCHITIS caused by smoke particles and increased mucus.

Carbon monoxide in the cigarette smoke gets picked up by the blood more easily than oxygen.

Arterial disease leads to heart attacks, strokes and even amputations.

Increased risk of chest infections.

- The tar in cigarette smoke contains CARCINOGENS (cancer inducing agents). These can cause lung cells to mutate to form tumours. In lung cancer the damaged cells can no longer control their divisions and the tumour or tumours grow larger.
- In emphysema, the side walls of the alveoli break down reducing the surface area for gas exchange. This means the sufferer must breathe more deeply in order to take in a greater volume of air to compensate for the reduced surface area. This forced inhalation and exhalation means more work for the intercostal muscles and as a result the chest takes on a barrel-shaped appearance.

Giving Up Smoking

It is perhaps too easy to condemn smokers outright for being weak-willed and lacking in mental resolve. Smoking for many people is a true addiction, and although this is more mental than physical, we should be prepared to offer encouragement to give up rather than abusing those who struggle to do so.
There are many possible ways in which a person can help themselves to give up ...

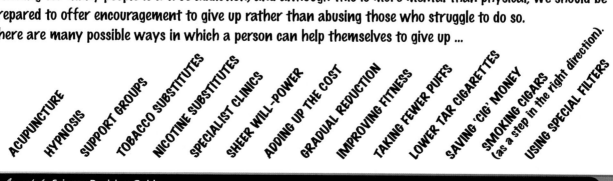

ACUPUNCTURE HYPNOSIS SUPPORT GROUPS TOBACCO SUBSTITUTES NICOTINE SUBSTITUTES SPECIALIST CLINICS SHEER WILL-POWER ADDING UP THE COST GRADUAL REDUCTION IMPROVING FITNESS TAKING FEWER PUFFS LOWER TAR CIGARETTES SAVING 'CIG' MONEY SMOKING CIGARS (as a step in the right direction) USING SPECIAL FILTERS

The Functions Of The Circulatory System

The circulatory system is the body's transport system. It transports the following ...

- CARBON DIOXIDE • OXYGEN • NUTRIENTS • WASTE PRODUCTS • HEAT • HORMONES.

However, primarily, it carries blood from the heart to all the cells of the body to provide them with FOOD and OXYGEN, and carries WASTE PRODUCTS including CARBON DIOXIDE away from the cells. Blood is pumped to the lungs so that CARBON DIOXIDE can be exchanged for OXYGEN.

- The system consists of THE HEART, THE BLOOD VESSELS and THE BLOOD.

The Layout Of The System

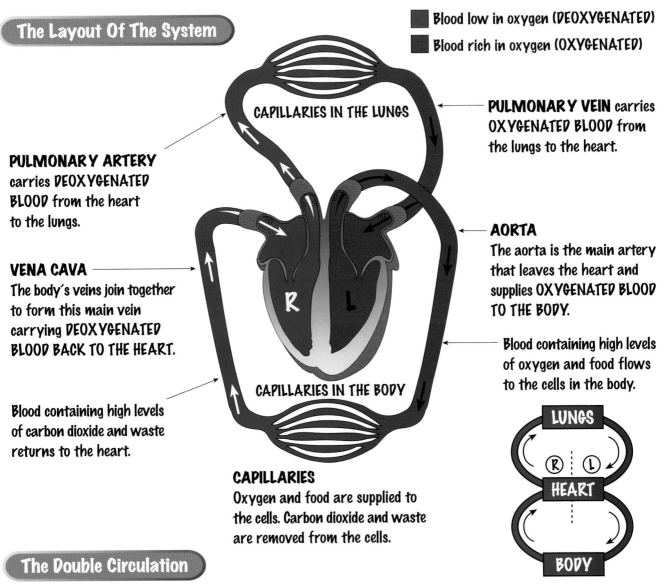

Blood low in oxygen (DEOXYGENATED)

Blood rich in oxygen (OXYGENATED)

CAPILLARIES IN THE LUNGS

PULMONARY VEIN carries OXYGENATED BLOOD from the lungs to the heart.

PULMONARY ARTERY carries DEOXYGENATED BLOOD from the heart to the lungs.

AORTA
The aorta is the main artery that leaves the heart and supplies OXYGENATED BLOOD TO THE BODY.

VENA CAVA
The body's veins join together to form this main vein carrying DEOXYGENATED BLOOD BACK TO THE HEART.

Blood containing high levels of oxygen and food flows to the cells in the body.

Blood containing high levels of carbon dioxide and waste returns to the heart.

CAPILLARIES IN THE BODY

CAPILLARIES
Oxygen and food are supplied to the cells. Carbon dioxide and waste are removed from the cells.

LUNGS

HEART

BODY

The Double Circulation

There are TWO SEPARATE CIRCULATORY SYSTEMS ...

| One which carries blood from the HEART to the LUNGS and then back to the HEART ... | ... and one which carries blood from the HEART to ALL OTHER PARTS OF THE BODY and then back to the HEART. |

- This means that blood flows around a 'figure of eight' circuit and passes through the heart TWICE on each circuit.
- Blood travels AWAY from the heart through the ARTERIES ...
- ... and returns to the heart through the VEINS.

| The LEFT SIDE of the heart pumps blood which is RICH IN OXYGEN and delivers it to all other parts of the BODY. | The RIGHT SIDE of the heart pumps blood which is LOW IN OXYGEN to the LUNGS, to pick up OXYGEN. |

The Heart In More Detail

The **HEART** is the main organ in the circulatory system and **PUMPS BLOOD** around the body.

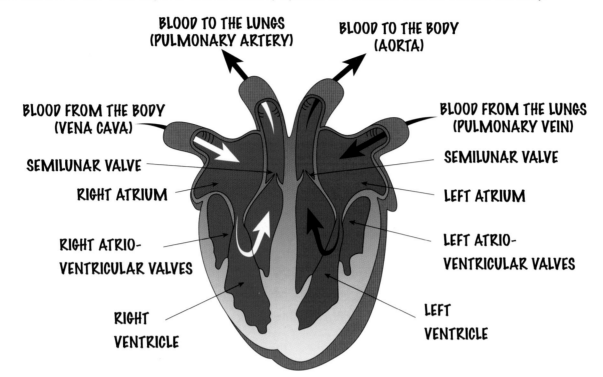

BLOOD TO THE LUNGS
(PULMONARY ARTERY)

BLOOD TO THE BODY
(AORTA)

BLOOD FROM THE BODY
(VENA CAVA)

BLOOD FROM THE LUNGS
(PULMONARY VEIN)

SEMILUNAR VALVE

SEMILUNAR VALVE

RIGHT ATRIUM

LEFT ATRIUM

RIGHT ATRIO-
VENTRICULAR VALVES

LEFT ATRIO-
VENTRICULAR VALVES

RIGHT
VENTRICLE

LEFT
VENTRICLE

- Most of the wall of the heart is made of **MUSCLE**.

- **ATRIA** are the smaller, **LESS MUSCULAR** upper chambers, which receive blood coming back to the heart through **VEINS**.

- **VENTRICLES** are the larger, **MORE MUSCULAR** lower chambers.
  The **LEFT** is more muscular than the right since it has to pump blood around the whole body.

- **VALVES** make sure that the blood flows in the right direction, and can't flow backwards.

How The Heart Pumps Blood

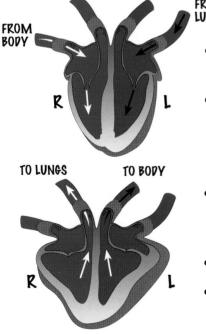

FROM
LUNGS

FROM
BODY

R   L

TO LUNGS   TO BODY

R   L

- When the **HEART MUSCLE RELAXES**, blood flows into the **ATRIA** from the **LUNGS** and the rest of the **BODY**.

- The **ATRIA** then **CONTRACT** squeezing blood into the **VENTRICLES**.

- When the **VENTRICLES CONTRACT** (squeeze) ...
  ... blood is forced out of the lower chambers into two arteries ...
  ... these carry blood to the body and the lungs.

- The blood can't flow backwards because of **VALVES** in the heart.

- The heart muscle now relaxes and the whole process starts again.

There are three types of blood vessels ... ARTERIES, VEINS and CAPILLARIES.
They form the 'plumbing' of the circulatory system.

Arteries

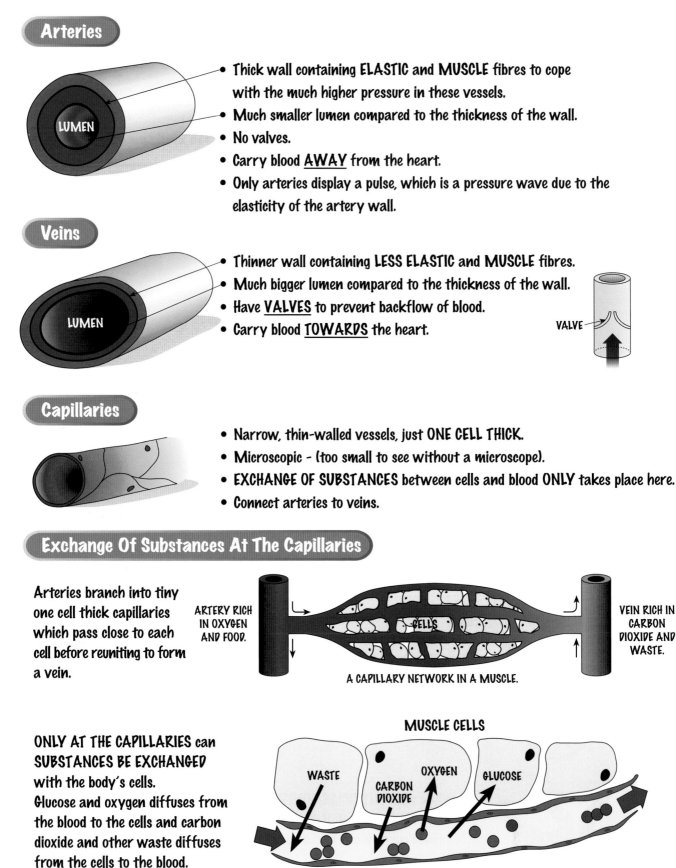

LUMEN

- Thick wall containing ELASTIC and MUSCLE fibres to cope with the much higher pressure in these vessels.
- Much smaller lumen compared to the thickness of the wall.
- No valves.
- Carry blood AWAY from the heart.
- Only arteries display a pulse, which is a pressure wave due to the elasticity of the artery wall.

Veins

LUMEN

- Thinner wall containing LESS ELASTIC and MUSCLE fibres.
- Much bigger lumen compared to the thickness of the wall.
- Have VALVES to prevent backflow of blood.
- Carry blood TOWARDS the heart.

VALVE

Capillaries

- Narrow, thin-walled vessels, just ONE CELL THICK.
- Microscopic - (too small to see without a microscope).
- EXCHANGE OF SUBSTANCES between cells and blood ONLY takes place here.
- Connect arteries to veins.

Exchange Of Substances At The Capillaries

Arteries branch into tiny one cell thick capillaries which pass close to each cell before reuniting to form a vein.

ARTERY RICH
IN OXYGEN
AND FOOD.

CELLS

VEIN RICH IN
CARBON
DIOXIDE AND
WASTE.

A CAPILLARY NETWORK IN A MUSCLE.

MUSCLE CELLS

ONLY AT THE CAPILLARIES can SUBSTANCES BE EXCHANGED with the body's cells.
Glucose and oxygen diffuses from the blood to the cells and carbon dioxide and other waste diffuses from the cells to the blood.

WASTE

CARBON
DIOXIDE

OXYGEN

GLUCOSE

A CAPILLARY VESSEL
(one cell thick)

Similarly carbon dioxide diffuses from the blood capillaries into the alveoli, while oxygen diffuses from the alveoli into the capillaries.

The Coronary Arteries

The coronary arteries supply blood directly to the heart muscle itself, in order to provide it with GLUCOSE and OXYGEN.

These substances are used in respiration to provide the energy that the heart muscle needs to contract. Anything which slows down the delivery of these substances will cause distress to the muscle tissue.

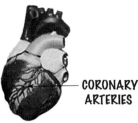

CORONARY ARTERIES

The delivery of oxygen depends on the red blood cells which carry it. They are specially adapted to do this job by having a bi-concave shape which gives them a bigger surface area through which oxygen can diffuse.

Coronary Heart Disease

Heart disease kills more people in Britain than any other disease. It is caused when a blockage occurs in one of the coronary arteries resulting in a restriction in the blood flow. Lack of oxygen results in damage to the muscle which may prove fatal.

This blockage usually occurs as a result of a gradual narrowing of the arteries due to one or more of the factors below. Eventually the artery becomes too narrow and the supply is restricted. More seriously, a small piece of fat may break off at some point and lodge in the narrowed vessel. This could prevent any blood flow and cause muscle cells to die. This could prove fatal.

Contributory Factors

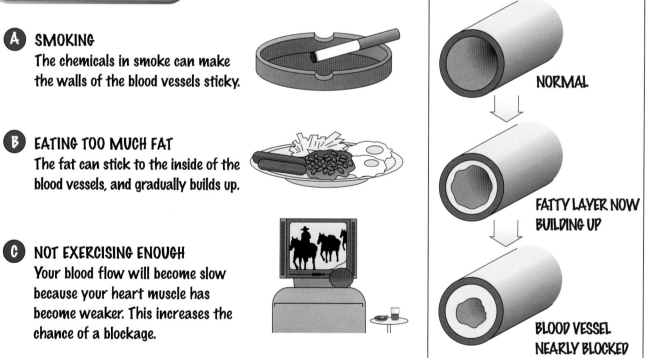

A SMOKING
The chemicals in smoke can make the walls of the blood vessels sticky.

B EATING TOO MUCH FAT
The fat can stick to the inside of the blood vessels, and gradually builds up.

C NOT EXERCISING ENOUGH
Your blood flow will become slow because your heart muscle has become weaker. This increases the chance of a blockage.

NORMAL

FATTY LAYER NOW BUILDING UP

BLOOD VESSEL NEARLY BLOCKED

Arteriosclerosis

This is the general name given to the process shown above where an artery starts to thicken and lose its elasticity. This can happen in any artery and can cause memory loss when it occurs in arteries in the brain, and numbness and lack of mobility when it occurs in the legs.

Diabetes

- DIABETES is a disease that is caused by the PANCREAS ...
  ... not producing and releasing ENOUGH INSULIN, which allows the blood sugar level to fluctuate.
- This can lead to a person's blood sugar level rising fatally HIGH ...
  ... resulting in a COMA.
- People who have DIABETES can CONTROL THEIR BLOOD SUGAR LEVEL by INJECTING INSULIN.
- Before INJECTING INSULIN a person with DIABETES will test the amount of SUGAR in their blood.
- If they have had FOOD containing A LOT OF SUGAR then a BIGGER DOSE OF INSULIN is required to reduce their BLOOD SUGAR LEVEL.
- If they are going to be VERY ACTIVE and use up a lot of SUGAR then a SMALLER DOSE OF INSULIN is required PRIOR TO THEM EXERCISING.

Control Of Blood Glucose

This is how different parts of the body WORK TOGETHER ...
... to MONITOR and CONTROL blood glucose levels.

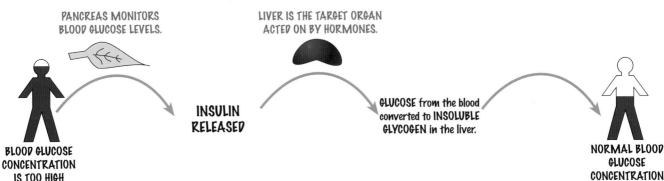

PANCREAS MONITORS
BLOOD GLUCOSE LEVELS.

LIVER IS THE TARGET ORGAN
ACTED ON BY HORMONES.

INSULIN
RELEASED

GLUCOSE from the blood
converted to INSOLUBLE
GLYCOGEN in the liver.

BLOOD GLUCOSE
CONCENTRATION
IS TOO HIGH

NORMAL BLOOD
GLUCOSE
CONCENTRATION

From the diagram, you can see that the pancreas produces insulin in response to a rise in glucose concentration. When the level falls, the pancreas produces less insulin.

---- HIGHER TIER ----

Producing Insulin Using Genetically Modified Bacteria

Human insulin can be produced by genetic engineering. The gene for insulin production is cut out of human DNA and inserted into a ring of bacterial DNA.

HUMAN INSULIN GENE INSERTED
INTO BACTERIAL DNA.

VAT

This is then replaced inside the bacterium which is then allowed to breed. Eventually there are millions of them, each programmed to produced insulin.

This method of producing insulin is a great breakthrough for diabetics. Not only can the insulin be made more cheaply, but it can be made in large quantities.

Prior to this, bovine insulin was used but people were understandably alarmed at being injected with cow hormones. This situation was worsened with the discovery of BSE being passed onto humans.

Also, bovine insulin was not always 100% effective and there could be side effects.

In spite of some opposition to genetic modification of organisms, this appears to be an example where only good has come of it.

Providing Oxygen To Cells

- The circulatory system carries oxygen from the lungs to all the body cells in order that energy can be released from glucose in AEROBIC respiration.
  This enables the working cells to have enough energy to do their work.

- During exercise, blood is pumped more vigorously around the body. In the lungs, oxygen is at a much higher concentration in the alveoli than in the blood, and so it quickly diffuses into the blood and combines with haemoglobin in the red cells. Carbon dioxide, meanwhile, diffuses from the blood (high concentration) to the alveoli.

- In respiring cells, such as working muscle cells, there is a higher concentration of oxygen and glucose in the blood than in the cell since the cell is using both of these in respiration. Consequently the haemoglobin releases its oxygen and the oxygen and glucose diffuse into the cell. At the same time carbon dioxide, which is being produced by the cell, diffuses into the blood ie. from a higher to a lower concentration.

Aerobic Respiration

... 'is the release of energy from the breakdown of glucose, ...
... by combining it with OXYGEN inside living cells.'
(The energy is actually contained inside the glucose molecule.)

THE EQUATION: **GLUCOSE + OXYGEN ⟹ CARBON DIOXIDE + WATER + ENERGY**

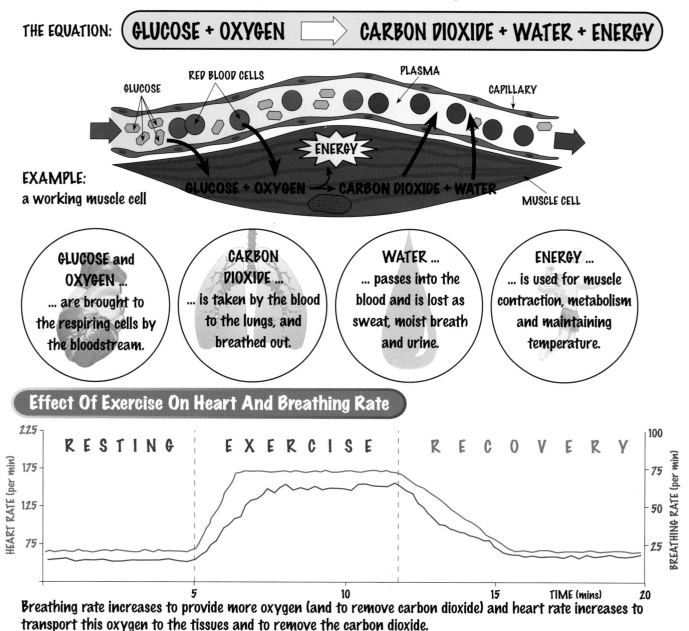

EXAMPLE:
a working muscle cell

GLUCOSE and OXYGEN ...
... are brought to the respiring cells by the bloodstream.

CARBON DIOXIDE ...
... is taken by the blood to the lungs, and breathed out.

WATER ...
... passes into the blood and is lost as sweat, moist breath and urine.

ENERGY ...
... is used for muscle contraction, metabolism and maintaining temperature.

Effect Of Exercise On Heart And Breathing Rate

Breathing rate increases to provide more oxygen (and to remove carbon dioxide) and heart rate increases to transport this oxygen to the tissues and to remove the carbon dioxide.

Anaerobic Respiration

... is the release of a little bit of energy, <u>very quickly</u>, inside living cells, from the INCOMPLETE breakdown of glucose in the ABSENCE OF OXYGEN.

THE EQUATION: **GLUCOSE ⟹ LACTIC ACID + A BIT OF ENERGY**

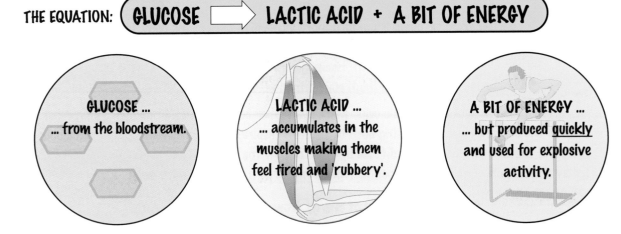

GLUCOSE ...
... from the bloodstream.

LACTIC ACID ...
... accumulates in the muscles making them feel tired and 'rubbery'.

A BIT OF ENERGY ...
... but produced **quickly** and used for explosive activity.

- This happens when the muscles are working so hard that...
- ...the lungs and bloodstream can't deliver enough OXYGEN, to respire the available glucose aerobically.
- Therefore the GLUCOSE can only be partly broken down, releasing a much smaller amount of energy...
- ... and LACTIC ACID as a waste product. It can only operate for a short time.
- Build up of lactic acid during vigorous activity causes acute fatigue in muscles, and results in 'OXYGEN DEBT'. This causes them to stop contracting efficiently. It must be broken down quickly to avoid cell damage.
- This 'debt' must be 'repaid' by continued deep breathing after exercise in order to provide enough oxygen to oxidise the lactic acid to carbon dioxide and water.

Some Facts About Anaerobic Respiration

- Anaerobic respiration is an inefficient process since it produces only $\frac{1}{20}$th as much energy as aerobic respiration (see previous page).
- However it produces energy MUCH FASTER and so is used during high intensity (explosive) activity over a <u>short period</u>.
- After a relatively short time, the build up of lactic acid affects the performance of the muscles.

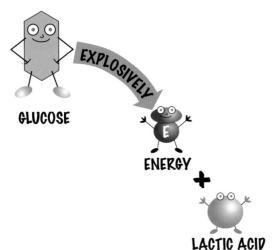

GLUCOSE

EXPLOSIVELY

ENERGY

+

LACTIC ACID

Steroid Abuse

Steroids (or anabolic agents) are substances which accelerate the growth and repair of muscle and as a consequence of this they are sometimes abused by athletes to help them to 'bulk up' for explosive events.

More recently there has been a worrying trend amongst young people who are using them to develop a better physique. The dangers with abuse of steroids include heart and blood pressure problems, excess aggression, male characteristics in females, loss of fertility, acne, menstrual irregularities, muscle cramps, liver problems and diabetes. QUITE SIMPLY IT'S NOT WORTH THE RISK!!!

Cystic Fibrosis And Sickle-cell Anaemia

Both of these conditions are inherited from the parents, though it is possible that neither of them have the condition themselves, since they are caused by recessive alleles.

Cystic fibrosis is a disorder of cell membranes causing thick and sticky mucus to be produced particularly in the LUNGS, GUT and PANCREAS. Too much mucus in these areas can lead to other complications.

Sickle-cell anaemia is a condition in which sufferers produce abnormally shaped red blood cells which look rather like a sickle. They experience general weakness and sometimes ANAEMIA. Carriers of the allele also show some degree of sickling but amazingly they have an increased resistance to malaria. This is an advantage in areas where malaria is widespread and this maintains the gene in the population.

HIGHER TIER

A Quick Recap On Genetics

You should really remember this from the module on INHERITANCE and SURVIVAL in volume 1. However just to remind you ...

- Genes are small sections of DNA which code for a particular characteristic.
- Alleles are alternative forms of a gene such as brown or blue eyes.
- Some alleles are dominant while others are recessive eg. Brown is dominant to blue in eye colour.
- The genes you inherit determine the characteristics you display.

Inheritance Of Cystic Fibrosis

Cystic fibrosis can be inherited if both parents are carrying the allele, which is recessive.

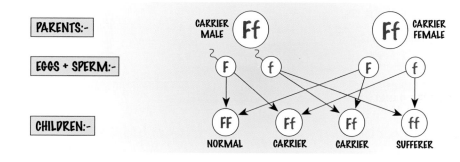

- This particular cross would result in a 1 in 4 chance of producing a sufferer.

Inheritance Of Sickle-cell Anaemia

Sickle-cell anaemia can also be inherited if both parents are carrying the allele, which is also recessive.

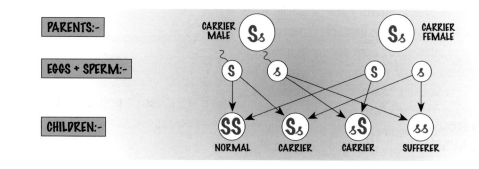

- Again, this particular cross would produce a 1 in 4 chance of producing a sufferer.

Gene Therapy

The aim of gene therapy is to treat diseases and disorders by modifying a person's genome. Obviously it would be virtually impossible to change the genes in every cell in the body but by targeting specific areas it is possible to provide some degree of cure. This is particularly true for conditions such as CYSTIC FIBROSIS which is caused by the presence of two recessive alleles.

Viruses are used in this technique, as vectors to deliver genetic material to the target cells. The viruses are attenuated ie. made harmless by removing their disease-causing component. The resulting modified virus cannot replicate itself inside the patient. In cystic fibrosis, too much mucus is made in the lungs so the lungs are targeted by the viral vector.

The process involves the following stages ...

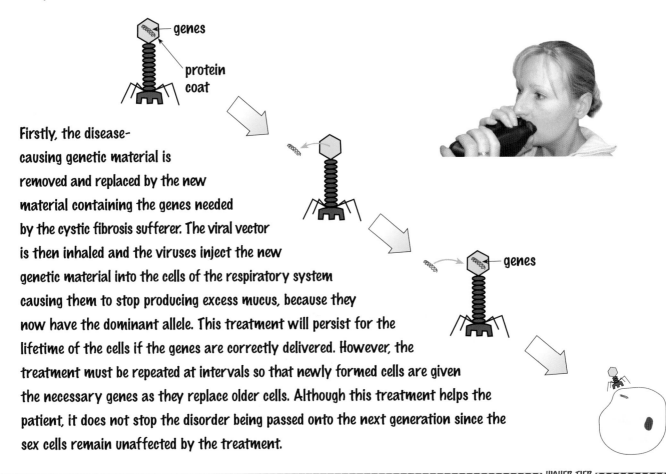

Firstly, the disease-causing genetic material is removed and replaced by the new material containing the genes needed by the cystic fibrosis sufferer. The viral vector is then inhaled and the viruses inject the new genetic material into the cells of the respiratory system causing them to stop producing excess mucus, because they now have the dominant allele. This treatment will persist for the lifetime of the cells if the genes are correctly delivered. However, the treatment must be repeated at intervals so that newly formed cells are given the necessary genes as they replace older cells. Although this treatment helps the patient, it does not stop the disorder being passed onto the next generation since the sex cells remain unaffected by the treatment.

HIGHER TIER

Genetic Counselling

In genetic counselling, the genetic background of a couple is studied in order to be able to identify the potential risks of a particular genetic disease occurring. This would usually involve a full pedigree analysis of each person in order to identify those members of their families who have had the disease. From this it is possible to work out who may be 'carriers' of the disease. This will then enable the counsellor to work out the probable genetic profile of each of the couple. He will then be able to predict the likelihood of the couple producing a child with the disease. It would then be up to the couple to decide whether to go ahead or not.

BREATHING SYSTEM AND VENTILATION

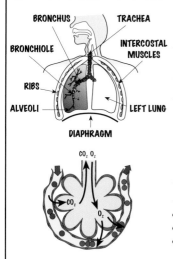

BRONCHUS — TRACHEA
BRONCHIOLE — INTERCOSTAL MUSCLES
RIBS
ALVEOLI — LEFT LUNG
DIAPHRAGM

INHALING
Intercostal muscles and diaphragm contract causing an increase in the volume of the thorax. This causes a decrease in pressure inside the thorax and atmospheric air enters.

EXHALING
Intercostal muscles and diaphragm relax causing a decrease in the volume of the thorax. This causes an increase in pressure inside the thorax and air is forced out.

The lungs are an excellent exchange surface because they have ...

- A MOIST PERMEABLE SURFACE.
- AN EXCELLENT BLOOD SUPPLY.
- A MASSIVE SURFACE AREA.

CO_2, O_2

In the alveoli, CO_2 diffuses from the blood into the lungs and O_2 diffuses from the lungs into the blood. The blood becomes oxygenated.

THE CIRCULATORY SYSTEM

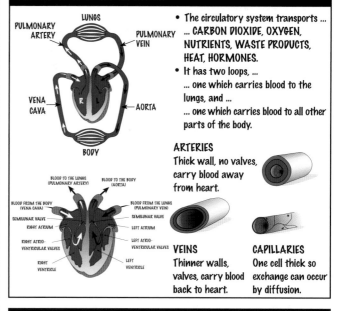

LUNGS
PULMONARY ARTERY — PULMONARY VEIN
VENA CAVA — AORTA
R L
BODY

- The circulatory system transports ... ... CARBON DIOXIDE, OXYGEN, NUTRIENTS, WASTE PRODUCTS, HEAT, HORMONES.
- It has two loops, ... one which carries blood to the lungs, and ... ... one which carries blood to all other parts of the body.

BLOOD TO THE LUNGS (PULMONARY ARTERY) BLOOD TO THE BODY (AORTA)
BLOOD FROM THE BODY (VENA CAVA) BLOOD FROM THE LUNGS (PULMONARY VEIN)
SEMILUNAR VALVE SEMILUNAR VALVE
RIGHT ATRIUM LEFT ATRIUM
RIGHT ATRIO-VENTRICULAR VALVES LEFT ATRIO-VENTRICULAR VALVES
RIGHT VENTRICLE LEFT VENTRICLE

ARTERIES
Thick wall, no valves, carry blood away from heart.

VEINS
Thinner walls, valves, carry blood back to heart.

CAPILLARIES
One cell thick so exchange can occur by diffusion.

SMOKING AND CIRCULATORY DISEASE

- Specialised cells in the respiratory system trap dust and bacteria by producing sticky mucus which is then wafted upwards away from the lungs by CILIA.

SMOKING
- Can cause cancer due to carcinogens in tar which can cause lung cells to mutate to form tumours.
- Can cause emphysema where the side walls of the alveoli break down reducing their surface area.
- Can cause bronchitis, arterial disease, chest infections, increased blood pressure and other forms of cancer.

CIRCULATORY DISEASE
Coronary arteries supply GLUCOSE and OXYGEN to the heart muscle. The oxygen is carried by the red blood cells which are bi-concave in shape to increase their surface area. Coronary vessels become blocked in heart disease. Contributory factors include SMOKING, EATING TOO MUCH FAT, LACK OF EXERCISE. These may lead to ARTERIOSCLEROSIS ...

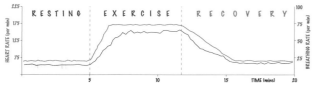

This can cause memory loss if it happens in the arteries of the brain and numbness and lack of mobility when it occurs in the legs.

INSULIN

Diabetes is caused by the pancreas producing insufficient insulin. This causes a rise in blood sugar. Diabetics must control their blood sugar by injecting insulin.

CONTROL OF BLOOD SUGAR

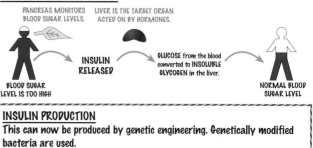

PANCREAS MONITORS BLOOD SUGAR LEVELS. LIVER IS THE TARGET ORGAN ACTED ON BY HORMONES.

BLOOD SUGAR LEVEL IS TOO HIGH INSULIN RELEASED GLUCOSE from the blood converted to INSOLUBLE GLYCOGEN in the liver. NORMAL BLOOD SUGAR LEVEL

INSULIN PRODUCTION
This can now be produced by genetic engineering. Genetically modified bacteria are used.

PART OF A HUMAN CHROMOSOME RING OF BACTERIAL DNA CUT OPEN HUMAN INSULIN GENE INSERTED INTO BACTERIAL DNA
HUMAN INSULIN GENE INSULIN GENE 'CUT OUT'

The bacterial DNA is then reinserted into the bacterium.

AEROBIC RESPIRATION AND ANAEROBIC RESPIRATION

AEROBIC RESPIRATION

GLUCOSE + OXYGEN ⟶ CARBON DIOXIDE + WATER + ENERGY

Heart rate and breathing rate increase with exercise as the circulatory system increases the supply of oxygen to the cells.

RESTING EXERCISE RECOVERY
HEART RATE (per min) / BREATHING RATE (per min)
TIME (mins) 5 10 15 20

ANAEROBIC RESPIRATION

GLUCOSE ⟶ LACTIC ACID + A BIT OF ENERGY

Occurs when muscles are working very hard and can operate only for a short time due to build up of lactic acid as a waste product. This results in acute fatigue and 'oxygen debt' which must be repaid by continued deep breathing after exercise. So that the lactic acid can be oxidised to carbon dioxide and water.

Not much energy but produced very quickly and therefore ideal in explosive activity.

GENETIC DISORDERS AND GENE THERAPY

CYSTIC FIBROSIS - too much mucus produced by lungs, gut and pancreas.
SICKLE-CELL ANAEMIA - sickle-shaped red cells cause anaemia but carriers have resistance to malaria.

INHERITANCE OF CYSTIC FIBROSIS - caused by a recessive allele.

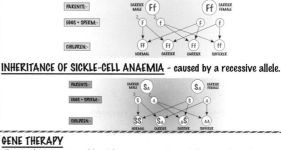

PARENTS:- CARRIER MALE Ff Ff CARRIER FEMALE
EGGS + SPERM:- F f F f
CHILDREN:- FF Ff Ff ff
NORMAL CARRIER CARRIER SUFFERER

INHERITANCE OF SICKLE-CELL ANAEMIA - caused by a recessive allele.

PARENTS:- CARRIER MALE S_s S_s CARRIER FEMALE
EGGS + SPERM S s S s
CHILDREN:- SS S_s sS ss
NORMAL CARRIER CARRIER SUFFERER

GENE THERAPY
This is the insertion of healthy genes into body cells to replace disease-causing alleles. Viral vectors are used to deliver the genetic material to the cells.

genes
protein coat
genes

- The treatment must be repeated at intervals because it only lasts for the lifetime of the cell.
- Also the offspring are still at risk from the disease.

Uses Of Metals

Many different metals are in use around us. Three of the most common ones are ...

IRON
(which is also used to make steel)

... for girders

... for cutlery

ALUMINIUM
(which is also used to make alloys)

... for window frames

... for aeroplanes

COPPER

... for pipes

... for wire

... for ornaments

(can be used to make brass, an alloy)

... for pans

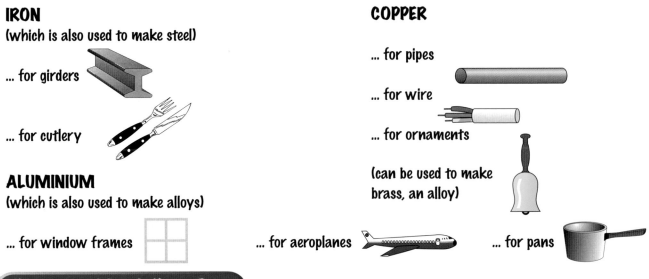

Extracting Metals From Ores

- Ores are naturally occurring rocks in the Earth's crust, which contain compounds of metals in sufficient amounts to make it worthwhile extracting them.
- The METHOD OF EXTRACTION depends on the metal's position in the REACTIVITY SERIES.

REACTIVITY SERIES	METHOD OF EXTRACTION
sodium calcium magnesium aluminium ~~CARBON~~	Energy is required to extract them from their ores, because they are very reactive metals. ELECTROLYSIS is used. Metals are formed at the cathode.
zinc iron copper	These metals are below carbon in the reactivity series and are extracted from their ores by heating with carbon/carbon monoxide.
gold platinum	These metals are unreactive and exist NATURALLY. They are obtained by physical processes eg. panning.

The most reactive metals are the most difficult to extract from their ores.

The least reactive metals are the easiest to extract from their ores.

Reduction

The process through which a metal compound is changed back to the metal element is called REDUCTION.
Reduction is the loss of oxygen from a compound ...

eg.

COPPER OXIDE + CARBON $\xrightarrow{\text{HEAT}}$ COPPER + CARBON DIOXIDE

$$2CuO_{(s)} + C_{(s)} \longrightarrow 2Cu_{(s)} + CO_{2(g)}$$

> ═══ HIGHER TIER ═══
>
> The copper is present in copper oxide as Cu^{2+} ions. To make this into copper metal, each ion must GAIN TWO ELECTRONS. This process is still called REDUCTION!
>
> so: $Cu^{2+} + 2e^- \longrightarrow Cu$
>
> When atoms or ions GAIN electrons, it is always called REDUCTION. When atoms or ions LOSE electrons it is always called OXIDATION. Remember OILRIG: Oxidation Is Loss, Reduction Is Gain.

Extraction Of Iron – The Blast Furnace

Iron is BELOW CARBON in the Reactivity Series.
It is one of the most widely used metals in the world
... for building, transport and everyday objects.
Haematite is the name of the ore from which iron is extracted.
It contains IRON (III) OXIDE.

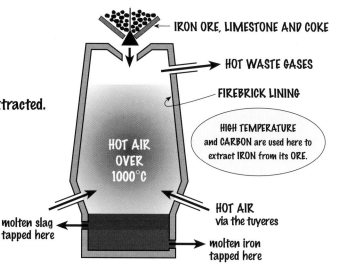

IRON ORE, LIMESTONE AND COKE

HOT WASTE GASES

FIREBRICK LINING

HIGH TEMPERATURE and CARBON are used here to extract IRON from its ORE.

HOT AIR OVER 1000°C

molten slag tapped here

HOT AIR via the tuyeres

molten iron tapped here

- HAEMATITE (iron ore), limestone and coke (carbon)
  are fed into the top of the furnace ...
  ... hot air is blasted in at the bottom.

- The CARBON REACTS WITH OXYGEN to form
  CARBON DIOXIDE and a great deal of heat energy.
  At these high temperatures the carbon dioxide will
  react with more carbon to form carbon monoxide.

- CARBON MONOXIDE IS A REDUCING AGENT and will take the oxygen from the iron oxide leaving just
  iron ie. it 'reduces' the iron oxide to molten iron which flows to the bottom of the furnace where it can
  be tapped off. Carbon itself is often used to reduce oxides as it is quite high in the Reactivity Series.
  However, here it is CARBON MONOXIDE which acts as the REDUCING AGENT.

  IRON OXIDE + CARBON MONOXIDE ⟶ IRON + CARBON DIOXIDE

- The limestone reacts with impurities, including sand, to form the slag. This can be used for a variety of
  purposes ... eg. filling in quarries, road-making, making building blocks.

Symbol Equations

These are the symbol equations for the reactions in the blast furnace. See if you can match them to the
correct stages above (for FOUNDATION TIER you should be able to BALANCE them GIVEN the formulae).

① $C_{(s)} + O_{2(g)} \longrightarrow CO_{2(g)}$ + **HEAT**

② $CO_{2(g)} + C_{(s)} \longrightarrow 2CO_{(g)}$

③ $Fe_2O_{3(s)} + 3CO_{(g)} \longrightarrow 2Fe_{(l)} + 3CO_{2(g)}$

④ $CaCO_{3(s)} \xrightarrow{\text{HEAT}} CaO_{(s)} + CO_{2(g)}$
Limestone

⑤ $CaO_{(s)} + SiO_{2(s)} \xrightarrow{\text{HEAT}} CaSiO_{3(l)}$
Slag

> ━━━━━━ HIGHER TIER ━━━━━━
> For HIGHER TIER you will be
> expected to be able to write
> these equations WITHOUT
> being given the formulae
> and also to identify any
> reduction reactions
> (see below).

Reduction ... A Reminder

- The loss of oxygen from an oxide is known as REDUCTION. In equation ③ above, the IRON (III) OXIDE
  is made up of two iron atoms chemically combined with three oxygen atoms. On reacting with carbon
  monoxide (CO) the iron (III) oxide is reduced to IRON which no longer has any oxygen atoms chemically
  combined with it.

Electrolysis

Some COMPOUNDS conduct electricity only when they are MOLTEN (melted) or in SOLUTION. In these cases the liquid or solution must contain IONS. If an electric current is passed through one of these liquids or solutions the compound will break up (decompose) and ELEMENTS will be produced.

When a DIRECT CURRENT is passed through a liquid containing ions, those which are POSITIVELY CHARGED move towards the negative CATHODE so they are called CATIONS. Those which are NEGATIVELY CHARGED move towards the positive ANODE so they are called ANIONS.

eg.

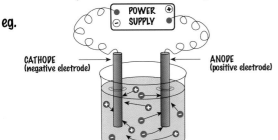

CATHODE (negative electrode)

ANODE (positive electrode)

POWER SUPPLY ⊕ ⊖

The general idea is ...

The ions move to the ELECTRODE of opposite charge, which follows the normal rules of electrostatics! When they get there, they lose their charges ... they are DISCHARGED. The negative ions LOSE electrons to the ANODE! The positive ions GAIN electrons from the CATHODE. During discharge ATOMS of ELEMENTS are formed.

- This process can be put to good use in industry eg. in the extraction of reactive metals from their ores ...

Extraction of Aluminium – By Electrolysis

- Aluminium must be obtained from its ore by electrolysis because it is too reactive to be extracted by heating with carbon. (Look at their positions in the Reactivity Series.)

The steps in the process are as follows ...

- ALUMINIUM ORE (BAUXITE) is purified to leave aluminium oxide.
- Aluminium oxide is MIXED WITH CRYOLITE (a compound of aluminium) TO LOWER ITS MELTING POINT.
- The aluminium oxide and cryolite mixture is melted ...
- ... so that the IONS CAN MOVE. This molten mixture is called the ELECTROLYTE.
- When a CURRENT passes through the molten mixture, the following happens ...
- AT THE NEGATIVE ELECTRODE (the CATHODE), ...
- ... POSITIVELY CHARGED ALUMINIUM IONS MOVE TOWARDS IT and ALUMINIUM FORMS and ...
- AT THE POSITIVE ELECTRODES (the ANODES), ...
- ... NEGATIVELY CHARGED OXIDE IONS MOVE TOWARDS THEM and OXYGEN FORMS.
- This causes the positive electrodes to burn away quickly as the carbon reacts with the oxygen, and they frequently have to be replaced.

POSITIVE CARBON ELECTRODE

CARBON LINING AS NEGATIVE ELECTRODE

STEEL TANK

ELECTROLYTE OF PURIFIED ALUMINIUM OXIDE IN MOLTEN CRYOLITE

TAP HOLE

MOLTEN ALUMINIUM

- This process is quite expensive because of the cost of the large amounts of DIRECT ELECTRIC CURRENT (15kWh for each kilogram of aluminium!) needed to carry it out.

During this process ... ALUMINIUM OXIDE $\longrightarrow$ ALUMINIUM + OXYGEN

In symbols this is ... $2Al_2O_{3(l)} \longrightarrow 4Al_{(l)} + 3O_{2(g)}$

HIGHER TIER

The reactions at the electrodes can be written as HALF EQUATIONS. This means that we write separate equations for what is happening at each of the electrodes during electrolysis.

So ... ELECTROLYSIS OF MOLTEN ALUMINIUM OXIDE ...

AT THE CATHODE: $Al^{3+}_{(l)} + 3e^- \xrightarrow{\text{REDUCTION}} Al_{(l)}$

AT THE ANODE: $2O^{2-}_{(l)} \xrightarrow{\text{OXIDATION}} O_{2(g)} + 4e^-$

The General Outline

- Copper can easily be extracted by REDUCTION but when it is needed in a pure form eg. for electrical circuits it is purified by ELECTROLYSIS.
- The POSITIVE ELECTRODE (the ANODE) is made of <u>impure</u> copper.
- The NEGATIVE ELECTRODE (the CATHODE) is made of <u>pure</u> copper.
- The solution MUST contain COPPER IONS. This is achieved using copper (II) sulphate solution as the electrolyte.

How Does It Work?

- AT THE **POSITIVE ELECTRODE** (the ANODE) COPPER IONS pass into the solution.
- AT THE **NEGATIVE ELECTRODE** (the CATHODE) COPPER IONS from the solution are attracted towards it ...
  ... TO FORM COPPER ATOMS which stick to the pure copper electrode.
- Consequently the negative electrode gets bigger and bigger as the positive electrode seems to 'dissolve' away to nothing. The pure copper cathode can then be removed for making into pipes/wire etc.
- The impurities in the positive electrode simply fall to the bottom as the process takes place. Some valuable metals are extracted from these impurities!

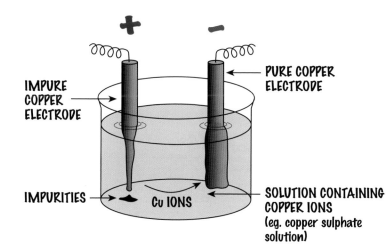

IMPURE COPPER ELECTRODE

PURE COPPER ELECTRODE

IMPURITIES

Cu IONS

SOLUTION CONTAINING COPPER IONS (eg. copper sulphate solution)

This is quite EXPENSIVE because of the cost of the electricity needed to carry out the process. This means that the resulting copper products are also expensive. There are limited resources of copper in the world, so we should conserve these as much as possible.

— HIGHER TIER —

Detailed Explanation

The solution of copper sulphate does <u>not</u> alter in concentration during the process ...
... if everything is working as it should.
The copper atoms change to copper (II) ions and leave the anode to go into solution ...
... at just the same rate that copper (II) ions arrive at the cathode and change to copper atoms.

SOLUTION CONTAINING COPPER IONS

At the NEGATIVE CATHODE:

$$Cu^{2+}_{(aq)} + 2e^- \xrightarrow{\text{REDUCTION}} Cu_{(s)}$$

blue copper (II) solution   gains two electrons   pinky brown copper metal

At the POSITIVE ANODE:

$$Cu_{(s)} \xrightarrow{\text{OXIDATION}} Cu^{2+}_{(aq)} + 2e^-$$

copper metal   blue copper (II) solution   loses two electrons

Transition Metals

- The TRANSITION METALS include all the elements between Group 2 and Group 3 in the Periodic Table.
- IRON and COPPER are well-known examples of transition elements and are located in the first (upper) row of the transition metal block.

Properties Of The Transition Metals

- Transition metal compounds are often coloured eg. copper sulphate crystals.
- Transition metals have high melting points eg. iron, copper and titanium all have melting points over 1000°C.
- Transition metals have high densities eg. copper has a density of **8.9 g/cm³**.
- Transition metals are good conductors of heat and electricity.

Uses Of The Transition Metals

In addition to their uses in things such as wire, girders, ornaments etc. the transition metals and their compounds are often used as catalysts. eg.

- In the Haber process an iron catalyst is used to speed up the reaction between nitrogen and hydrogen to make ammonia gas.
- In the contact process vanadium (V) oxide (V_2O_5) is used to speed up the reaction between sulphur dioxide (SO_2) and oxygen (O_2) during the manufacture of sulphuric acid.

Alkali Metals

- The ALKALI METALS occupy the first vertical group (GROUP 1) at the left hand side of the Periodic Table.
- LITHIUM, SODIUM and POTASSIUM are typical members of this group.

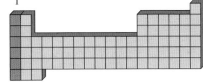

Properties Of The Alkali Metals

- They have LOW MELTING POINTS eg. potassium has a melting point of 63°C and are SOFT.
- They react VIGOROUSLY with water to form HYDROXIDES which are alkaline (pH > 7) and hydrogen gas.
- Their high degree of reactivity means they must be stored under oil.
- The FURTHER DOWN group 1 the metal is, the GREATER its REACTIVITY, so the most reactive is at the bottom. Lithium is the least reactive alkali metal.

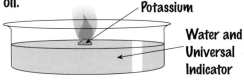

POTASSIUM + WATER ⟶ POTASSIUM HYDROXIDE + HYDROGEN

Electrolysis Of Sodium Chloride Solution

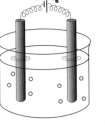

If a DIRECT CURRENT is passed through a concentrated SOLUTION of sodium chloride (rock salt) THREE main products are obtained.

❶ CHLORINE at the positive electrode.
❷ HYDROGEN at the negative electrode. This is used for manufacturing MARGARINE and AMMONIA.
❸ SODIUM HYDROXIDE which remains in the solution and is used in making SOAP, PAPER and SYNTHETIC FIBRES.

NB SODIUM CHLORIDE itself is used for de-icing roads, in the food industry and for making sodium hydroxide.

Types Of Rock

GRANITE
(Large crystals)

BASALT
(Small crystals)

IGNEOUS ROCK ... is formed from molten magma which has either come to the surface or has been trapped beneath it. These rocks are very hard and consist of interlocking crystals which are large if the rock has cooled slowly and small if it has cooled quickly. Due to the way they were formed, igneous rocks do NOT CONTAIN ANY FOSSILS.

SEDIMENTARY ROCK ... is formed when particles of any type of rock are carried by water to the sea where they form layers which become cemented together (the shells of tiny dead organisms can also form these layers). The oldest layers therefore are usually at the bottom with the age of the layers decreasing as you get to the uppermost one. These rocks may contain fossils which can be used to date the rocks.

LIMESTONE   **SANDSTONE**

SLATE   **MARBLE**

METAMORPHIC ROCK ... is usually formed from sedimentary rocks which have been subjected to high temperature and pressure. This changes their structure (without melting them!) and they become harder and denser. They may contain fossils which have been distorted by these conditions. When metamorphic rocks are formed they are only changed in physical ways (eg. crystal structure, density), they are NOT changed chemically. eg. LIMESTONE and MARBLE are both forms of calcium carbonate.

The Big Picture

The formation of the three main types of rock are summarised in the diagram below ...

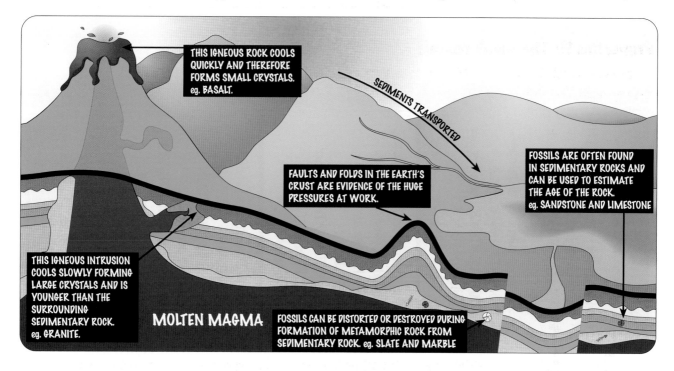

THIS IGNEOUS ROCK COOLS QUICKLY AND THEREFORE FORMS SMALL CRYSTALS. eg. BASALT.

SEDIMENTS TRANSPORTED

FAULTS AND FOLDS IN THE EARTH'S CRUST ARE EVIDENCE OF THE HUGE PRESSURES AT WORK.

FOSSILS ARE OFTEN FOUND IN SEDIMENTARY ROCKS AND CAN BE USED TO ESTIMATE THE AGE OF THE ROCK. eg. SANDSTONE AND LIMESTONE

THIS IGNEOUS INTRUSION COOLS SLOWLY FORMING LARGE CRYSTALS AND IS YOUNGER THAN THE SURROUNDING SEDIMENTARY ROCK. eg. GRANITE.

MOLTEN MAGMA

FOSSILS CAN BE DISTORTED OR DESTROYED DURING FORMATION OF METAMORPHIC ROCK FROM SEDIMENTARY ROCK. eg. SLATE AND MARBLE

The diagram above shows the ways in which the three main types of rock are formed. Because sedimentary rock originates on the sea-bed it often contains fossils. The high temperature and pressure which converts this to metamorphic rock often destroys or distorts the fossils in it.

The following table summarises the main CHARACTERISTICS, FEATURES and METHODS OF FORMATION of some of the most common examples of each rock type.

	EXAMPLES	SPECIFIC FEATURES OF THESE EXAMPLES	WHAT THEY LOOK LIKE	HOW THEY'RE FORMED
SEDIMENTARY	SANDSTONE	Formed by particles of SAND, washed down by rivers, eventually falling to RIVER BEDS or SEA BEDS.	• Very GRAINY and CRUMBLY. • SANDGRAINS OBVIOUS. • Sometimes contains FOSSILS ... • ... which can be used to DATE rocks.	• Made from layers of SEDIMENT (small particles) ... • ... whose WEIGHT squeezes out WATER ... • ... causing particles to become 'CEMENTED' together ... • YOUNGER ROCKS therefore are usually ON TOP.
	LIMESTONE	Formed by DEAD REMAINS of SHELLED CREATURES and some INSOLUBLE CALCIUM SALTS. eg. calcium carbonate	• GRAINY + CRUMBLY but less than above. • Often contain FOSSILS ... • ...which can be used to DATE rocks.	
IGNEOUS	BASALT	Expelled from VOLCANOES. Formed by rapid cooling ABOVE the Earth's crust.	• Very SMALL CRYSTALS due to FAST COOLING. • Never contain fossils.	• Formed from MOLTEN ROCK ... • ... called MAGMA ... • ... which wells up from the MANTLE ... • ... and COOLS DOWN, either ... • ... ABOVE or WITHIN the Earth's crust.
	GRANITE	Magma forced into the Earth's crust. Formed by slow cooling WITHIN the Earth's crust.	• LARGE CRYSTALS due to SLOW COOLING. • Never contain fossils.	
METAMORPHIC	SLATE	Formed when MUDSTONE experiences EXTREME TEMPERATURE and PRESSURE.	• Tiny CRYSTALS form on COOLING. • Usually HARD rocks. • Could contain distorted fossils.	• Formed by extreme TEMP. and PRESSURE ... • ... caused by MOUNTAIN BUILDING processes ... • ... which force SEDIMENTARY rocks deep underground ... • ... close to MAGMA ... • ... where they become COMPRESSED and HEATED ... • ... changing their TEXTURE and STRUCTURE. • Can be formed from any rock type.
	MARBLE	Formed when LIMESTONE experiences EXTREME TEMPERATURE and PRESSURE.	• Small CRYSTALS form on COOLING. • Usually HARD rocks. • Could contain distorted fossils.	

You need to study the table carefully and make sure you UNDERSTAND the way in which each type of rock is formed and, as a result, why each has the appearance it has and behaves in the way that it does.

Since the formation of the Earth 4.6 billion years ago the atmosphere has changed very dramatically.
The timescale, however, is enormous because one billion years is one thousand million years! (1,000,000,000)

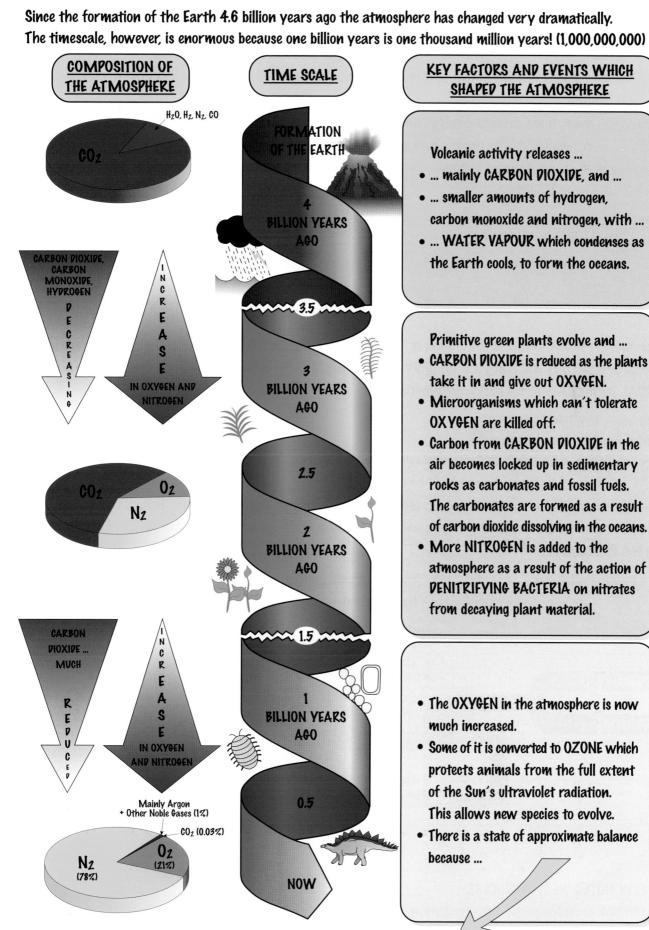

COMPOSITION OF THE ATMOSPHERE

H_2O, H_2, N_2, CO

CO_2

CARBON DIOXIDE, CARBON MONOXIDE, HYDROGEN — DECREASING

INCREASE IN OXYGEN AND NITROGEN

CO_2 O_2
N_2

CARBON DIOXIDE ... MUCH REDUCED

INCREASE IN OXYGEN AND NITROGEN

Mainly Argon
+ Other Noble Gases (1%)

CO_2 (0.03%)

N_2
(78%)

O_2
(21%)

TIME SCALE

FORMATION OF THE EARTH

4 BILLION YEARS AGO

3.5

3 BILLION YEARS AGO

2.5

2 BILLION YEARS AGO

1.5

1 BILLION YEARS AGO

0.5

NOW

KEY FACTORS AND EVENTS WHICH SHAPED THE ATMOSPHERE

Volcanic activity releases ...
• ... mainly CARBON DIOXIDE, and ...
• ... smaller amounts of hydrogen, carbon monoxide and nitrogen, with ...
• ... WATER VAPOUR which condenses as the Earth cools, to form the oceans.

Primitive green plants evolve and ...
• CARBON DIOXIDE is reduced as the plants take it in and give out OXYGEN.
• Microorganisms which can't tolerate OXYGEN are killed off.
• Carbon from CARBON DIOXIDE in the air becomes locked up in sedimentary rocks as carbonates and fossil fuels. The carbonates are formed as a result of carbon dioxide dissolving in the oceans.
• More NITROGEN is added to the atmosphere as a result of the action of DENITRIFYING BACTERIA on nitrates from decaying plant material.

• The OXYGEN in the atmosphere is now much increased.
• Some of it is converted to OZONE which protects animals from the full extent of the Sun's ultraviolet radiation. This allows new species to evolve.
• There is a state of approximate balance because ...

• PHOTOSYNTHESIS produces oxygen in the presence of sunlight.
• RESPIRATION and BURNING FUELS use oxygen and produce CARBON DIOXIDE
• CARBON DIOXIDE is absorbed by the SEAS and OCEANS.

Making Ammonia

- Ammonia is an ALKALINE gas which is LIGHTER than air and has an unpleasant smell.
- It has the formula NH_3 which tells us it consists of two elements, NITROGEN and HYDROGEN, chemically joined together.
- However, to get these gases to combine chemically, AND STAY COMBINED, is very difficult.
- The main reason for this is that the elements combine in what is called a REVERSIBLE REACTION. This means that as well as nitrogen and hydrogen combining with each other, the ammonia formed also DECOMPOSES under the same conditions.

Equations

Words: NITROGEN   +   HYDROGEN $\rightleftharpoons$ AMMONIA

Symbols: $N_{2(g)}$ + $3H_{2(g)}$ $\rightleftharpoons$ $2NH_{3(g)}$

The $\rightleftharpoons$ symbol indicates the process is 'REVERSIBLE', but it also indicates that if the chemicals are in a 'closed system' they will reach a stage of DYNAMIC EQUILIBRIUM where the RATE of the forward reaction is EQUAL TO the RATE of the backward reaction.

Why Make Ammonia?

The production of ammonia and nitric acid are intermediate steps in the production of ammonium nitrate FERTILISER. Until 1908 nitrogen couldn't be turned into nitrates on a large scale, and the world was quickly running out of fertilisers, even though air is 78% nitrogen! It was a German scientist, Fritz Haber, who first worked out a way of making ammonia on a large scale. Below is a simplified version of the HABER PROCESS.

The raw materials are:- • NITROGEN - from the fractional distillation of liquid air.
• HYDROGEN - from natural gas and steam.

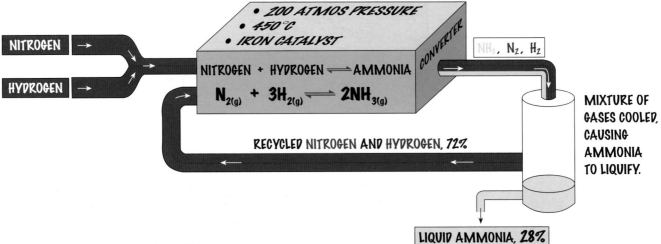

A FEW NOTES ON THIS PROCESS
- The high pressure 'pushes' the equilibrium position from left to right.
- The catalyst increases the rate at which equilibrium is reached.
- The temperature is chosen to give a good RATE of ammonia production without making it decompose too much.

HIGHER TIER

There is great economic importance attached to getting the MAXIMUM AMOUNT of AMMONIA in the SHORTEST POSSIBLE TIME. This demands a degree of COMPROMISE.

Effect Of Temperature And Pressure On The Production Of Ammonia

The forward reaction is EXOTHERMIC. It gives out heat.
The backward reaction is ENDOTHERMIC. It takes in heat.

$$\text{EXOTHERMIC} \longrightarrow \text{HEAT OUT}$$
$$N_{2(g)} + 3H_{2(g)} \rightleftharpoons 2NH_{3(g)}$$
$$\text{ENDOTHERMIC} \longleftarrow \text{HEAT IN}$$

EFFECT OF TEMPERATURE 1

Because the formation of ammonia is exothermic, ... LOW TEMPERATURE WOULD FAVOUR THE PRODUCTION OF AMMONIA ... which would increase the yield.

EFFECT OF TEMPERATURE 2

Increasing the temperature increases the rate of reaction equally in both directions, therefore ...
... HIGH TEMPERATURE WOULD MAKE AMMONIA FORM FASTER (and break down faster!)

EFFECT OF PRESSURE

Increased pressure means increased concentration and therefore faster reaction rate. Also since four molecules are being changed into two molecules, increasing the pressure favours the smaller volume. Therefore ... HIGH PRESSURE FAVOURS THE PRODUCTION OF AMMONIA, ... but too high a pressure is expensive to MAINTAIN and CONTAIN.

A Compromise Solution

In reality, ...
- ... A LOW TEMPERATURE INCREASES YIELD BUT THE REACTION IS TOO SLOW.
- ... A HIGH PRESSURE INCREASES YIELD BUT THE REACTION IS TOO EXPENSIVE.
- ... A CATALYST INCREASES THE RATE AT WHICH EQUILIBRIUM IS REACHED BUT DOES NOT AFFECT YIELD.

So, a COMPROMISE is reached in the Haber process ...

| TEMPERATURE = 450°C | PRESSURE = 200 ATMOSPHERES | CATALYST = IRON |

Fertilisers

Ammonia can be converted to NITRIC ACID (HNO_3).
More ammonia can be used to NEUTRALISE the nitric acid to produce AMMONIUM NITRATE - a fertiliser.
AMMONIUM SULPHATE can also be used as a fertiliser. It can be made by using ammonia to neutralise SULPHURIC ACID.
Plants need nitrogen for healthy growth - but they can't use the nitrogen from the air as it is INERT.
Farmers use artificial fertilisers to replace the nitrogen in the soil which has been used up by previous crops, this means that crop yields can be increased. However ...
- ... excessive use of fertilisers can cause problems.
- ... high nitrate content in drinking water can be harmful.
- ... nitrates leaching into lakes and rivers causes EUTROPHICATION ie. ...

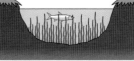

Nitrates cause excessive plant growth.

The plants die and start to rot.

The rotting process uses up oxygen and the water cannot support life.

- The NOBLE GASES are located in a vertical group at the right-hand end of the Periodic Table.
- This is called Group VIII (8) or Group 0 depending on which book or chart you look at!
- ALL the elements in Group 8 are CHEMICALLY INERT ie. unreactive, compared with elements in other groups of the Periodic Table.

Reactivity In Group 8

- The Noble Gases all have ...
  ... FULL OUTERMOST ENERGY LEVELS ...
  ... therefore they DO NOT need to lose or gain electrons in reactions to become stable and ...
  ... so they do not react with many other elements.
  If we take the first three noble gases ...

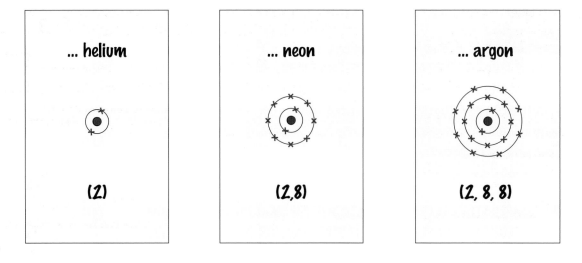

... helium

(2)

... neon

(2,8)

... argon

(2, 8, 8)

Uses Of The Noble Gases

Because these gases are very UNREACTIVE, don't have a SMELL, and can't be SEEN ...
... they were not discovered until about 1898.
Most of their uses are based on two things ...

1 They are unreactive
2 They glow with a particular colour when electricity passes through them.

- Helium is used in airships and weather balloons because it is much less dense than air and non-flammable.

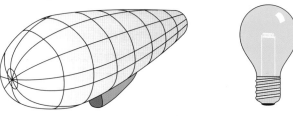

- Argon is used in light bulbs because it is unreactive and provides an inert atmosphere.

- Argon, krypton and neon are all used in fluorescent lights and discharge tubes.

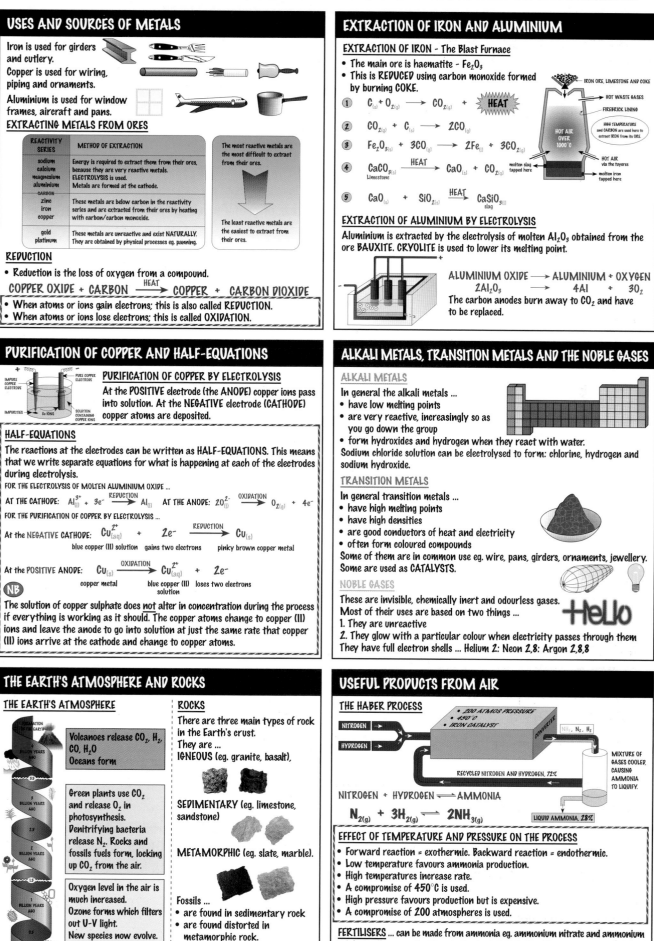

USES AND SOURCES OF METALS

Iron is used for girders and cutlery.

Copper is used for wiring, piping and ornaments.

Aluminium is used for window frames, aircraft and pans.

EXTRACTING METALS FROM ORES

REACTIVITY SERIES	METHOD OF EXTRACTION
sodium calcium magnesium aluminium	Energy is required to extract them from their ores, because they are very reactive metals. ELECTROLYSIS is used. Metals are formed at the cathode.
CARBON	
zinc iron copper	These metals are below carbon in the reactivity series and are extracted from their ores by heating with carbon/carbon monoxide.
gold platinum	These metals are unreactive and exist NATURALLY. They are obtained by physical processes eg. panning.

The most reactive metals are the most difficult to extract from their ores.

The least reactive metals are the easiest to extract from their ores.

REDUCTION

• Reduction is the loss of oxygen from a compound.

COPPER OXIDE + CARBON $\xrightarrow{HEAT}$ COPPER + CARBON DIOXIDE

• When atoms or ions gain electrons; this is also called REDUCTION.
• When atoms or ions lose electrons; this is called OXIDATION.

EXTRACTION OF IRON AND ALUMINIUM

EXTRACTION OF IRON - The Blast Furnace

• The main ore is haematite - Fe_2O_3
• This is REDUCED using carbon monoxide formed by burning COKE.

(1) $C_{(s)} + O_{2(g)} \longrightarrow CO_{2(g)} +$ HEAT

(2) $CO_{2(g)} + C_{(s)} \longrightarrow 2CO_{(g)}$

(3) $Fe_2O_{3(s)} + 3CO_{(g)} \longrightarrow 2Fe_{(l)} + 3CO_{2(g)}$

(4) $CaCO_{3(s)} \xrightarrow{HEAT} CaO_{(s)} + CO_{2(g)}$
Limestone

(5) $CaO_{(s)} + SiO_{2(s)} \xrightarrow{HEAT} CaSiO_{3(l)}$
slag

IRON ORE, LIMESTONE AND COKE
HOT WASTE GASES
FIREBRICK LINING
HIGH TEMPERATURE and CARBON are used to extract IRON from its ORE
HOT AIR OVER 1000°C
HOT AIR via the tuyeres
molten slag tapped here
molten iron tapped here

EXTRACTION OF ALUMINIUM BY ELECTROLYSIS

Aluminium is extracted by the electrolysis of molten Al_2O_3 obtained from the ore BAUXITE. CRYOLITE is used to lower its melting point.

ALUMINIUM OXIDE $\longrightarrow$ ALUMINIUM + OXYGEN
$2Al_2O_3 \longrightarrow 4Al + 3O_2$

The carbon anodes burn away to CO_2 and have to be replaced.

PURIFICATION OF COPPER AND HALF-EQUATIONS

+ IMPURE COPPER ELECTRODE — PURE COPPER ELECTRODE
IMPURITIES — Cu IONS — SOLUTION CONTAINING COPPER IONS

PURIFICATION OF COPPER BY ELECTROLYSIS

At the POSITIVE electrode (the ANODE) copper ions pass into solution. At the NEGATIVE electrode (CATHODE) copper atoms are deposited.

HALF-EQUATIONS

The reactions at the electrodes can be written as HALF-EQUATIONS. This means that we write separate equations for what is happening at each of the electrodes during electrolysis.

FOR THE ELECTROLYSIS OF MOLTEN ALUMINIUM OXIDE ...

AT THE CATHODE: $Al^{3+}_{(l)} + 3e^- \xrightarrow{REDUCTION} Al_{(l)}$ AT THE ANODE: $2O^{2-}_{(l)} \xrightarrow{OXIDATION} O_{2(g)} + 4e^-$

FOR THE PURIFICATION OF COPPER BY ELECTROLYSIS ...

At the NEGATIVE CATHODE: $Cu^{2+}_{(aq)} + 2e^- \xrightarrow{REDUCTION} Cu_{(s)}$
blue copper (II) solution   gains two electrons   pinky brown copper metal

At the POSITIVE ANODE: $Cu_{(s)} \xrightarrow{OXIDATION} Cu^{2+}_{(aq)} + 2e^-$
copper metal   blue copper (II) solution   loses two electrons

(NB) The solution of copper sulphate does not alter in concentration during the process if everything is working as it should. The copper atoms change to copper (II) ions and leave the anode to go into solution at just the same rate that copper (II) ions arrive at the cathode and change to copper atoms.

ALKALI METALS, TRANSITION METALS AND THE NOBLE GASES

ALKALI METALS

In general the alkali metals ...
• have low melting points
• are very reactive, increasingly so as you go down the group
• form hydroxides and hydrogen when they react with water.

Sodium chloride solution can be electrolysed to form: chlorine, hydrogen and sodium hydroxide.

TRANSITION METALS

In general transition metals ...
• have high melting points
• have high densities
• are good conductors of heat and electricity
• often form coloured compounds

Some of them are in common use eg. wire, pans, girders, ornaments, jewellery. Some are used as CATALYSTS.

NOBLE GASES

These are invisible, chemically inert and odourless gases. Most of their uses are based on two things ...
1. They are unreactive
2. They glow with a particular colour when electricity passes through them

Hello

They have full electron shells ... Helium 2: Neon 2,8: Argon 2,8,8

THE EARTH'S ATMOSPHERE AND ROCKS

THE EARTH'S ATMOSPHERE

OXIDATION OF IRON IN CRUST
4.5 BILLION YEARS AGO
Volcanoes release CO_2, H_2, CO, H_2O
Oceans form

3.5 BILLION YEARS AGO
Green plants use CO_2 and release O_2 in photosynthesis. Denitrifying bacteria release N_2. Rocks and fossils fuels form, locking up CO_2 from the air.

2 BILLION YEARS AGO
Oxygen level in the air is much increased. Ozone forms which filters out U-V light. New species now evolve. Respiration, burning fuels, photosynthesis balance out O_2 and CO_2 in the air.

NOW

ROCKS

There are three main types of rock in the Earth's crust. They are ...

IGNEOUS (eg. granite, basalt),

SEDIMENTARY (eg. limestone, sandstone)

METAMORPHIC (eg. slate, marble).

Fossils ...
• are found in sedimentary rock
• are found distorted in metamorphic rock.
When metamorphic rocks change structure they are not changed chemically.

USEFUL PRODUCTS FROM AIR

THE HABER PROCESS

• 200 ATMOS PRESSURE
• 450°C
• IRON CATALYST

NITROGEN
HYDROGEN
CONVERTER
NH_3, N_2, H_2

MIXTURE OF GASES COOLER, CAUSING AMMONIA TO LIQUIFY.

RECYCLED NITROGEN AND HYDROGEN, 72%

LIQUID AMMONIA, 28%

NITROGEN + HYDROGEN $\rightleftharpoons$ AMMONIA

$N_{2(g)} + 3H_{2(g)} \rightleftharpoons 2NH_{3(g)}$

EFFECT OF TEMPERATURE AND PRESSURE ON THE PROCESS

• Forward reaction = exothermic. Backward reaction = endothermic.
• Low temperature favours ammonia production.
• High temperatures increase rate.
• A compromise of 450°C is used.
• High pressure favours production but is expensive.
• A compromise of 200 atmospheres is used.

FERTILISERS ... can be made from ammonia eg. ammonium nitrate and ammonium sulphate. These supply nitrogen to plants in solution. However excess nitrates in drinking water are harmful. Nitrates in lakes/rivers cause excessive plant growth and eventually this kills all organisms.

This page is similar to work covered in module 3 and 6 of volume 1, but there are important differences.

The Atom

- Atoms are the 'basic' particles from which all matter is built.
- Atoms have a small NUCLEUS consisting of PROTONS and NEUTRONS (one exception) surrounded by ELECTRONS.
- These particles which make up atoms have different relative masses and charges ...

ATOMIC PARTICLE	RELATIVE MASS	RELATIVE CHARGE
PROTON	1	1+
NEUTRON	1	0
ELECTRON	0 (nearly!)	1-

- ALL the atoms of a particular element have the same number of protons in their nuclei. This is called the ATOMIC NUMBER.
- MASS NUMBER is the total number of PROTONS and NEUTRONS in the atom.

A Simple Example – Helium

NEUTRON
- Neutral - no charge.
- Same mass as a proton.

PROTON
- Positively charged.
- An atom has the same number of protons as electrons ...
... so the atom as a whole has no electrical charge.
- Same mass as a neutron.

ELECTRON
- Negatively charged.
- Same number of electrons as protons.
- Mass negligible ie. nearly nothing!

- Atoms of an element can be described very conveniently; take the helium atom above ...

MASS NUMBER
NUMBER OF PROTONS AND NEUTRONS → 4

ATOMIC NUMBER
NUMBER OF PROTONS → 2

$$^4_2\text{He}$$

ELEMENT SYMBOL
IN THIS CASE, THE ELEMENT HELIUM

Isotopes

The number of protons defines the element.
However, some atoms of the SAME ELEMENT can have DIFFERENT NUMBERS OF NEUTRONS; these are called ISOTOPES. Because they have the same number of protons and electrons they have the same chemical properties. They are easy to spot because they have the SAME ATOMIC NUMBER but a DIFFERENT MASS NUMBER.

FOR EXAMPLE

Chlorine has 2 isotopes ...

 $^{35}_{17}\text{Cl}$ ... has 18 neutrons

$^{37}_{17}\text{Cl}$ 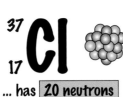 ... has 20 neutrons

Carbon has 2 isotopes ...

$^{12}_{6}\text{C}$  ... has 6 neutrons

$^{14}_{6}\text{C}$ 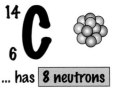 ... has 8 neutrons

- Remember, in an isotope the number of neutrons differ ...
... but because the isotopes of an element have the same electron configuration their reactions are the same.

HIGHER TIER

Relative Atomic Mass

Naturally occurring chlorine consists of about 75% of $^{35}_{17}\text{Cl}$ and 25% of $^{37}_{17}\text{Cl}$ ie. in the ratio of about 3:1.
Chemists use RELATIVE ATOMIC MASSES which take into account the RELATIVE ISOTOPIC MASSES and the ABUNDANCE of each one. So, if we take chlorine as an example ...
For every 4 atoms of chlorine, 3 of them are $^{35}_{17}\text{Cl}$ and 1 of them is $^{37}_{17}\text{Cl}$.

Total atomic mass of these 4 atoms = 3 x 35 + 1 x 37 = 142

RELATIVE ATOMIC MASS OF CHLORINE = $\frac{142}{4}$ = 35.5

NB The relative atomic mass is often NOT a whole number (as above for chlorine) whereas the relative isotopic masses for that element always are.

Forming Compounds

A COMPOUND is a substance which is formed from TWO or MORE ELEMENTS which have been joined together in a chemical reaction. All compounds can be identified by their FORMULA. This tells us the ratio of the ATOMS of each element in the compound.

If we consider what happens when a mixture of IRON and SULPHUR is heated ...

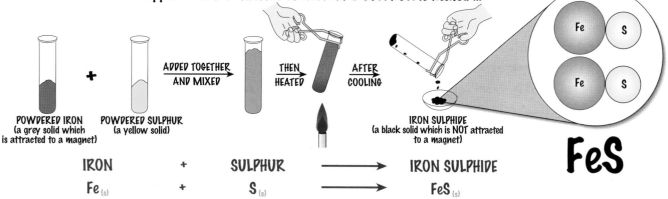

| POWDERED IRON (a grey solid which is attracted to a magnet) | POWDERED SULPHUR (a yellow solid) | ADDED TOGETHER AND MIXED | THEN HEATED | AFTER COOLING | IRON SULPHIDE (a black solid which is NOT attracted to a magnet) |

$$IRON \quad + \quad SULPHUR \quad \longrightarrow \quad IRON \ SULPHIDE$$
$$Fe_{(s)} \quad + \quad S_{(s)} \quad \longrightarrow \quad FeS_{(s)}$$

FeS

ie. one atom of iron plus one atom of sulphur produces iron sulphide. The ways in which compounds behave (their properties) are VERY DIFFERENT from the elements from which they were formed. Once formed compounds can only be split into simpler substances (elements) through chemical reactions.

Other Examples

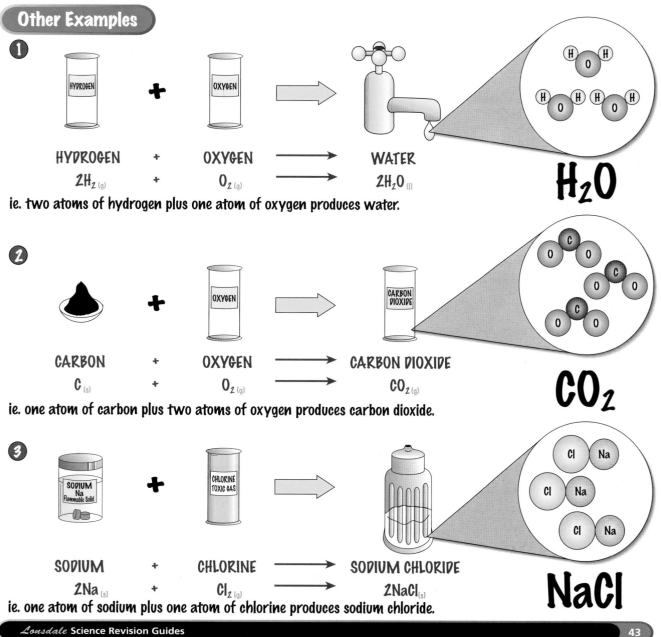

1

$$HYDROGEN \quad + \quad OXYGEN \quad \longrightarrow \quad WATER$$
$$2H_{2(g)} \quad + \quad O_{2(g)} \quad \longrightarrow \quad 2H_2O_{(l)}$$

H₂O

ie. two atoms of hydrogen plus one atom of oxygen produces water.

2

$$CARBON \quad + \quad OXYGEN \quad \longrightarrow \quad CARBON \ DIOXIDE$$
$$C_{(s)} \quad + \quad O_{2(g)} \quad \longrightarrow \quad CO_{2(g)}$$

CO₂

ie. one atom of carbon plus two atoms of oxygen produces carbon dioxide.

3

$$SODIUM \quad + \quad CHLORINE \quad \longrightarrow \quad SODIUM \ CHLORIDE$$
$$2Na_{(s)} \quad + \quad Cl_{2(g)} \quad \longrightarrow \quad 2NaCl_{(s)}$$

NaCl

ie. one atom of sodium plus one atom of chlorine produces sodium chloride.

IONIC BONDING

- To become chemically stable, atoms lose or gain electrons to fill their outermost energy levels or shells.
- These electrons must be accepted by, or 'donated' by, other atoms.
- Sometimes electrons are COMPLETELY TRANSFERRED. This results in the formation of an IONIC BOND.
- Sometimes electrons are SHARED between atoms forming a COVALENT BOND.

The Ionic Bond

- This occurs between a METAL and a NON-METAL ATOM ...
- ... and involves a TRANSFER OF ELECTRONS from one atom to the other ...
- ... to form electrically charged 'atoms' called IONS ...
- ... each of which has a 'COMPLETE' OUTER ELECTRON SHELL, just like the very unreactive noble gases.

__EXAMPLE 1__ SODIUM AND CHLORINE ... to form SODIUM CHLORIDE.

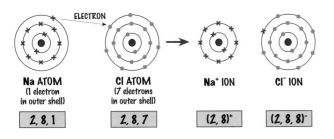

The SODIUM (Na) ATOM has 1 ELECTRON in its OUTER SHELL ...
... which is TRANSFERRED to the CHLORINE (Cl) ATOM.
BOTH now have 8 ELECTRONS in their OUTER SHELL.
The atoms are now IONS ...
... Na^+ and Cl^- ...
... and the COMPOUND FORMED is ...
... SODIUM CHLORIDE, NaCl.

__EXAMPLE 2__ MAGNESIUM AND OXYGEN ... to form MAGNESIUM OXIDE.

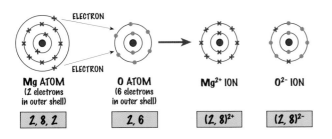

The MAGNESIUM (Mg) ATOM has 2 ELECTRONS in its OUTER SHELL ...
... which are TRANSFERRED to the OXYGEN (O) ATOM.
BOTH now have 8 ELECTRONS in their OUTER SHELL.
The atoms are now IONS ...
... Mg^{2+} and O^{2-} ...
... and the COMPOUND FORMED is ...
... MAGNESIUM OXIDE, MgO.

Properties Of Ionic Compounds

Ionic compounds, like sodium chloride, consist of a giant lattice held together by the forces of attraction between POSITIVE sodium ions (+) and NEGATIVE chloride ions (-).

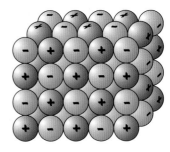

Magnesium oxide consists of a similar giant lattice but made up of Mg^{2+} and O^{2-} ions.

Ionic compounds ...
- ... have high melting points due to the STRONG ELECTROSTATIC FORCES of attraction which hold them together.
- ... conduct electricity when molten or in solution because the charged ions are free to MOVE ABOUT.
- ... often, but not always, dissolve in water. When they do dissolve, strong forces of attraction are formed between the IONS and the WATER.
- ... are CRYSTALLINE due to the regular arrangement of their ions.

NB
Sodium chloride dissolves in water while magnesium oxide is insoluble.

The Covalent Bond

- The covalent bond occurs between NON-METAL atoms and forms a very strong bond in which ELECTRONS ARE SHARED.
- It can occur between atoms of the same element or atoms from different elements.
- It results in the formation of MOLECULES.

EXAMPLES

<u>CHLORINE ATOMS</u>: join together to form <u>CHLORINE MOLECULES</u> (Cl_2).

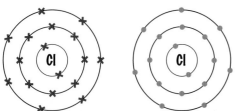

Shared pair
of electrons

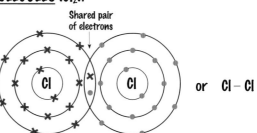

or   Cl – Cl

The atoms BOTH need to gain an electron
to fill their outermost energy levels ...

... they achieve this by sharing one pair
of electrons in a COVALENT BOND.

<u>NITROGEN ATOMS</u>: join together to form <u>NITROGEN MOLECULES</u> (N_2).

or $N \equiv N$

The atoms BOTH need to gain THREE electrons
to fill their outermost energy levels ...

... they achieve this by sharing THREE pairs
of electrons in a TRIPLE COVALENT BOND.

Other Examples (Outermost shells only)

<u>Water (H_2O)</u>

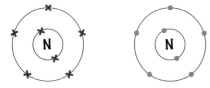

H – O – H

<u>Hydrogen (H_2)</u>

H – H

<u>Methane (CH_4)</u>

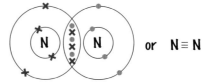

H – C – H

<u>Oxygen (O_2)</u>

O = O

ONE DOUBLE BOND

<u>Hydrogen Chloride (HCl)</u>

H – Cl

HIGHER TIER

<u>Carbon Dioxide (CO_2)</u>

O = C = O

TWO DOUBLE BONDS

Properties Of Simple Covalently Bonded Molecules

The covalent bond BETWEEN the two ATOMS is VERY
STRONG but the attraction between MOLECULES is WEAK.
This means that simple molecules ...
... have low melting and boiling points, ...
... have no overall electric charge so they CANNOT
   conduct electricity.

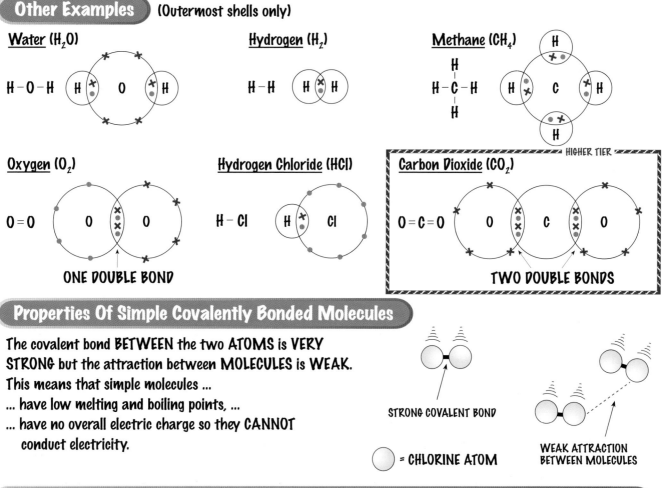

STRONG COVALENT BOND

= CHLORINE ATOM

WEAK ATTRACTION
BETWEEN MOLECULES

Simple Molecules

- These are molecules with relatively few atoms. There are STRONG FORCES between the ATOMS in the molecules but ONLY WEAK FORCES BETWEEN the molecules themselves.

FOR EXAMPLE ...

HEAT →

The molecules come apart from each other EASILY. In fact iodine boils at 184°C but the COVALENT BONDS within the molecules do NOT break!

IODINE SOLID ($I_{2(s)}$)   IODINE VAPOUR ($I_{2(g)}$)

- At room temperature many substances exist as GASES usually made up of molecules consisting of more than one atom. Again, there are STRONG covalent bonds within them, but virtually no force of attraction BETWEEN them.

eg.   Nitrogen   Oxygen   Ammonia

Covalent Giant Structures

These may have many, many atoms joined to each other COVALENTLY throughout the 'whole structure'. This makes their properties very different from those of the simple molecules shown above.

Diamond (A Form Of Carbon)

COVALENT BOND BETWEEN TWO CARBON ATOMS

● CARBON ATOM

- A GIANT, RIGID COVALENT STRUCTURE (LATTICE) where each carbon atom ...
- ... forms FOUR COVALENT BONDS with other carbon atoms.
- The large number of covalent bonds results in diamond having a VERY HIGH MELTING POINT.

Graphite (A Form Of Carbon)

- A GIANT COVALENT STRUCTURE (LATTICE) in which each carbon atom ...
- ... forms THREE COVALENT BONDS with other carbon atoms ...
- ... in a layered structure in which layers can slide past each other.
- Between layers there are weak forces of attraction ...
- ... resulting in free electrons and so graphite CONDUCTS ELECTRICITY.

COVALENT BOND BETWEEN TWO CARBON ATOMS

WEAK BOND BETWEEN LAYERS

● CARBON ATOM

Silicon Dioxide, SiO_2 (Silica)

COVALENT BOND   ○ SILICON ATOM
                        ● OXYGEN ATOM

(This is a very simple diagram of its structure)

- A GIANT COVALENT STRUCTURE (LATTICE) similar to diamond where each oxygen atom is joined ...
- ... to two silicon atoms and each silicon atom is joined to four oxygen atoms.
- The large number of covalent bonds results in silicon dioxide having a VERY HIGH MELTING POINT.

Temperature Changes

Many chemical reactions are accompanied by a temperature change.

● **EXOTHERMIC REACTIONS ...**

... are accompanied by a TEMPERATURE RISE. They are known as EXOTHERMIC reactions because THERMAL (HEAT) ENERGY is transferred OUT TO THE SURROUNDINGS. Combustion is a common example of an exothermic reactions ...

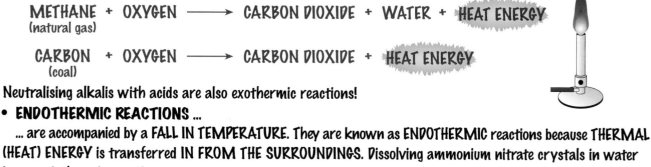

METHANE + OXYGEN ⟶ CARBON DIOXIDE + WATER + HEAT ENERGY
(natural gas)

CARBON + OXYGEN ⟶ CARBON DIOXIDE + HEAT ENERGY
(coal)

Neutralising alkalis with acids are also exothermic reactions!

● **ENDOTHERMIC REACTIONS ...**

... are accompanied by a FALL IN TEMPERATURE. They are known as ENDOTHERMIC reactions because THERMAL (HEAT) ENERGY is transferred IN FROM THE SURROUNDINGS. Dissolving ammonium nitrate crystals in water is an endothermic reaction ...

AMMONIUM NITRATE + WATER ⟶ AMMONIUM NITRATE SOLUTION − HEAT ENERGY

The temperature has fallen by 7°C!

The reaction between citric acid and sodium hydrogen carbonate solution is also an endothermic reaction.

HIGHER TIER

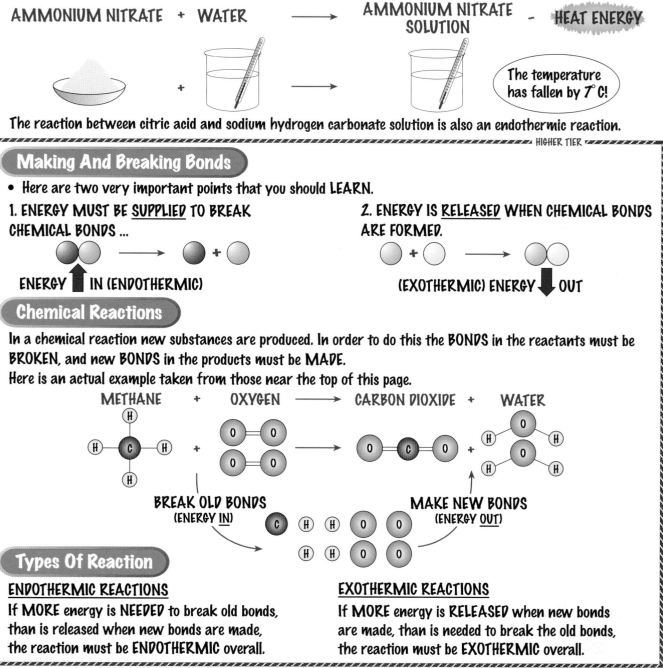

Making And Breaking Bonds

● Here are two very important points that you should LEARN.

1. ENERGY MUST BE SUPPLIED TO BREAK CHEMICAL BONDS ...

ENERGY ⬆ IN (ENDOTHERMIC)

2. ENERGY IS RELEASED WHEN CHEMICAL BONDS ARE FORMED.

(EXOTHERMIC) ENERGY ⬇ OUT

Chemical Reactions

In a chemical reaction new substances are produced. In order to do this the BONDS in the reactants must be BROKEN, and new BONDS in the products must be MADE.

Here is an actual example taken from those near the top of this page.

METHANE + OXYGEN ⟶ CARBON DIOXIDE + WATER

BREAK OLD BONDS (ENERGY IN)

MAKE NEW BONDS (ENERGY OUT)

Types Of Reaction

ENDOTHERMIC REACTIONS

If MORE energy is NEEDED to break old bonds, than is released when new bonds are made, the reaction must be ENDOTHERMIC overall.

EXOTHERMIC REACTIONS

If MORE energy is RELEASED when new bonds are made, than is needed to break the old bonds, the reaction must be EXOTHERMIC overall.

Relative Atomic Mass, A_r

Atoms are too small for their actual atomic mass to be of much use to us. To make things more manageable we use RELATIVE ATOMIC MASS, A_r. Basically this is just the MASS OF A PARTICULAR ATOM compared to the MASS OF AN ATOM OF HYDROGEN, the lightest atom of all. In fact we now use 1/12th the mass of a CARBON ATOM, but it doesn't make any real difference!

If we look at the PERIODIC TABLE below we can see that all the elements have TWO NUMBERS.

Here are some common elements ...

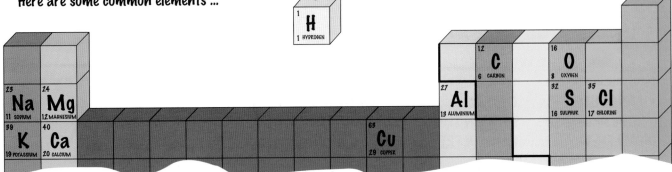

- The larger of the two numbers is the **MASS NUMBER** of the element but ...
  ... it also very conveniently doubles as the **RELATIVE ATOMIC MASS**, A_r of the element.
- So, in the examples above carbon is twelve times heavier than hydrogen, but ...
  ... is only half as heavy as magnesium, which is three quarters as heavy as sulphur ...
  ... which is twice as heavy as oxygen and so on, and so on ...
- We can use this idea to calculate the RELATIVE FORMULA MASS of compounds.

Relative Formula Mass, M_r

The relative formula mass of a compound is simply the relative atomic masses of all its elements added together. To calculate M_r, we need the FORMULA OF THE COMPOUND, and the A_r of ALL THE ATOMS INVOLVED.

EXAMPLE 1 - Using the data above, find the M_r of water, H_2O

STEP 1:	the formula ...	H_2O
STEP 2:	the A_r's ...	$(2 \times 1) + 16$
STEP 3:	the M_r ...	$2 + 16 = \underline{18}$

Since water has an M_r of 18, it is 18 times heavier than a hydrogen atom, or 1.5 times heavier than a carbon atom, or $2/3$ as heavy as an aluminium atom.

EXAMPLE 2 - Using the data above, find the M_r of sodium hydroxide, NaOH

STEP 1:	the formula ...	NaOH
STEP 2:	the A_r's ...	$23 + 16 + 1$
STEP 3:	the M_r ...	$23 + 16 + 1 = \underline{40}$

Since sodium hydroxide has an M_r of 40, it is as heavy as a calcium atom!

EXAMPLE 3 - Using the data above, find the M_r of potassium carbonate, K_2CO_3

STEP 1:	the formula ...	K_2CO_3
STEP 2:	the A_r's ...	$(39 \times 2) + 12 + (16 \times 3)$
STEP 3:	the M_r ...	$78 + 12 + 48 = \underline{138}$

We sometimes need to be able to work out how much of a substance is USED UP or PRODUCED in a chemical reaction, when we are given certain data. To do this we need to know ...

- ... the RELATIVE FORMULA MASS, M_r of the REACTANTS and PRODUCTS (or the A_r of all the elements.)
- ... the BALANCED SYMBOL EQUATION for the reaction concerned.

By substituting the first of these into the second we can work out ...

THE RATIO OF MASS OF REACTANT TO MASS OF PRODUCT

... and then apply this ratio to the question.

Calculating The Mass Of A Product

EXAMPLE - How much calcium oxide can be produced from 50Kg of calcium carbonate?
(Relative Atomic Masses: Ca = 40, C = 12, O = 16)

STEP 1: Write down the equation.

$$CaCO_{3(s)} \xrightarrow{\text{HEAT}} CaO_{(s)} + CO_{2(g)}$$

STEP 2: Work out the M_r of each substance.

$$40 + 12 + (3 \times 16) \longrightarrow (40 + 16) + [12 + (2 \times 16)]$$

STEP 3: CHECK the total mass of reactants = the total mass of the products. If they are not the same, check your work.

$$100 \longrightarrow 56 + 44 \checkmark$$

Since the question only mentions calcium oxide and calcium carbonate, you can now ignore the carbon dioxide!

This gives us ... ... THE RATIO OF MASS OF REACTANT ... $100 \longrightarrow 56$ ... TO MASS OF PRODUCT

STEP 4: Apply this ratio to the question ...

... If 100Kg of $CaCO_3$ produces 56Kg of CaO ...

... then 1Kg $CaCO_3$ produces $\frac{56}{100}$ Kg of CaO ...

... and 50Kg of $CaCO_3$ produces $\frac{56}{100} \times 50$ = <u>28Kg of CaO</u>.

Calculating The Mass Of A Reactant

EXAMPLE - How much aluminium oxide is needed to produce 540 tonnes of aluminium?
(Relative Atomic Masses: Al = 27, O = 16).

STEP 1: Write down the equation.

$$2 Al_2 O_{3(l)} \longrightarrow 4 Al_{(l)} + 3 O_{2(g)}$$

STEP 2: Work out the M_r of each substance.

$$2[(2 \times 27) + (3 \times 16)] \longrightarrow (4 \times 27) + [3 \times (2 \times 16)]$$

STEP 3: <u>CHECK</u> the total mass of reactants = the total mass of the products

$$204 \longrightarrow 108 + 96 \checkmark$$

Since the question only mentions aluminium oxide and aluminium, you can now ignore the oxygen!

This gives us ... ... THE RATIO OF MASS OF REACTANT $204 \longrightarrow 108$ TO MASS OF PRODUCT

STEP 4: Apply this ratio to the question ...

... If 204 tonnes of $Al_2 O_3$ produces 108 tonnes of Al ...

... then $\frac{204}{108}$ tonnes is needed to produce 1 tonne of Al ...

... and $\frac{204}{108} \times 540$ tonnes is needed to produce 540 tonnes of Al.

i.e. <u>1020 tonnes of $Al_2 O_3$ is needed</u>

HIGHER TIER

The Empirical Formula is the simplest formula which represents the RATIO OF ATOMS IN A COMPOUND.
There's one simple rule ...

ALWAYS DIVIDE THE DATA YOU ARE GIVEN BY THE A_r OF THE ELEMENT.

You then simplify the ratio to give you the simplest formula.

EXAMPLE 1

Find the simplest formula of an oxide of iron, formed by reacting 2.24g of iron with 0.96g of oxygen.
(Relative Atomic Masses: Fe = 56, O = 16).

| STEP 1: | Divide the masses by A_r | For iron $\dfrac{2.24}{56}$ | For oxygen $\dfrac{0.96}{16}$ |

| STEP 2: | Write down the ratio | 0.04 : 0.06 |

| STEP 3: | Simplify this ratio | 2 : 3 |

| STEP 4: | Write formula | Simplest Formula is Fe_2O_3 |

EXAMPLE 2

Find the simplest formula of an oxide of magnesium which contains 60% magnesium and 40% oxygen by weight
(Relative Atomic Masses: Mg = 24, O = 16).

Just treat the percentages as if they were grams ...

| STEP 1: | Divide the masses by A_r | For magnesium $\dfrac{60}{24}$ | For oxygen $\dfrac{40}{16}$ |

| STEP 2: | Write down the ratio | 2.5 : 2.5 |

| STEP 3: | Simplify this ratio | 1 : 1 |

| STEP 4: | Write formula | Simplest Formula is MgO |

EXAMPLE 3

Find the simplest formula of a compound which contains 10g of calcium, 3g of carbon and 12g of oxygen.
(Relative Atomic Masses: Ca = 40, C = 12, O = 16).

| STEP 1: | Divide the masses by A_r | For calcium $\dfrac{10}{40}$ For carbon $\dfrac{3}{12}$ For oxygen $\dfrac{12}{16}$ |

| STEP 2: | Write down the ratio | 0.25 : 0.25 : 0.75 |

| STEP 3: | Simplify this ratio | 1 : 1 : 3 |

| STEP 4: | Write formula | Simplest Formula is $CaCO_3$ |

EXAMPLE 4

Find the simplest formula of a compound which contains 1.2g of magnesium, 1.6g of oxygen and 0.1g of hydrogen.
(Relative Atomic Masses: Mg = 24, O = 16, H = 1).

| STEP 1: | Divide the masses by A_r | For magnesium $\dfrac{1.2}{24}$ For oxygen $\dfrac{1.6}{16}$ For hydrogen $\dfrac{0.1}{1}$ |

| STEP 2: | Write down the ratio | 0.05 : 0.1 : 0.1 |

| STEP 3: | Simplify this ratio | 1 : 2 : 2 |

| STEP 4: | Write formula | Simplest Formula is $Mg(OH)_2$ and NOT MgO_2H_2 !! |

ATOMS AND ISOTOPES

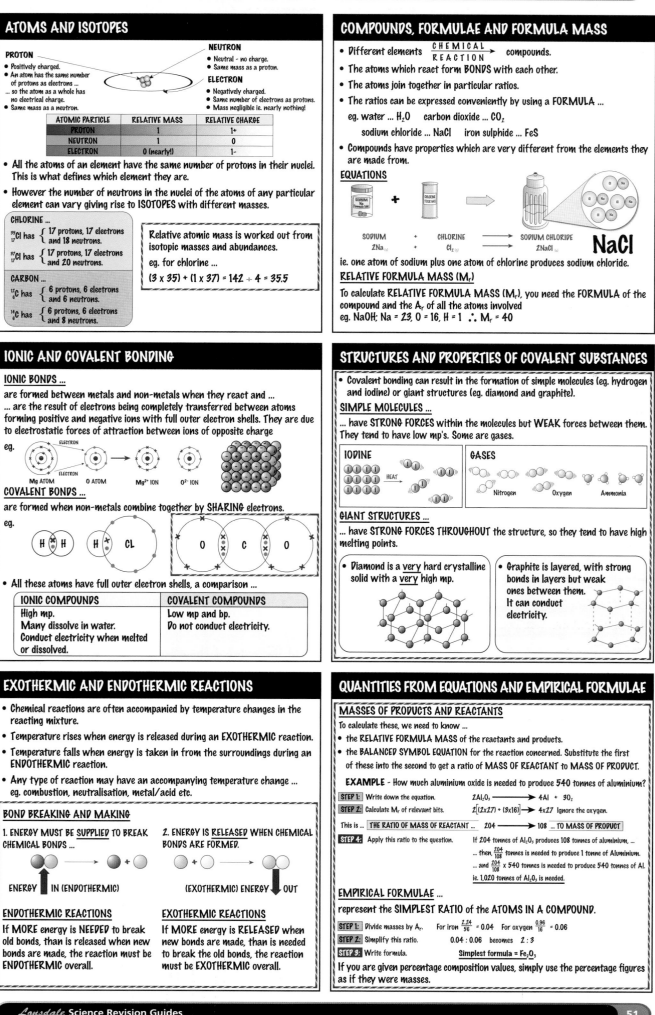

PROTON
- Positively charged.
- An atom has the same number of protons as electrons ...
  ... so the atom as a whole has no electrical charge.
- Same mass as a neutron.

NEUTRON
- Neutral - no charge.
- Same mass as a proton.

ELECTRON
- Negatively charged.
- Same number of electrons as protons.
- Mass negligible ie. nearly nothing!

ATOMIC PARTICLE	RELATIVE MASS	RELATIVE CHARGE
PROTON	1	1+
NEUTRON	1	0
ELECTRON	0 (nearly!)	1-

- All the atoms of an element have the same number of protons in their nuclei. This is what defines which element they are.
- However the number of neutrons in the nuclei of the atoms of any particular element can vary giving rise to ISOTOPES with different masses.

CHLORINE ...
$^{35}_{17}Cl$ has { 17 protons, 17 electrons and 18 neutrons.
$^{37}_{17}Cl$ has { 17 protons, 17 electrons and 20 neutrons.

CARBON ...
$^{12}_{6}C$ has { 6 protons, 6 electrons and 6 neutrons.
$^{14}_{6}C$ has { 6 protons, 6 electrons and 8 neutrons.

Relative atomic mass is worked out from isotopic masses and abundances.
eg. for chlorine ...
$(3 \times 35) + (1 \times 37) = 142 \div 4 = 35.5$

COMPOUNDS, FORMULAE AND FORMULA MASS

- Different elements $\xrightarrow{\text{CHEMICAL REACTION}}$ compounds.
- The atoms which react form BONDS with each other.
- The atoms join together in particular ratios.
- The ratios can be expressed conveniently by using a FORMULA ...
  eg. water ... H_2O carbon dioxide ... CO_2
  sodium chloride ... NaCl   iron sulphide ... FeS
- Compounds have properties which are very different from the elements they are made from.

EQUATIONS

SODIUM   +   CHLORINE   →   SODIUM CHLORIDE   **NaCl**
$2Na_{(s)}$ + $Cl_{2(g)}$ → $2NaCl_{(s)}$

ie. one atom of sodium plus one atom of chlorine produces sodium chloride.

RELATIVE FORMULA MASS (M_r)
To calculate RELATIVE FORMULA MASS (M_r), you need the FORMULA of the compound and the A_r of all the atoms involved
eg. NaOH; Na = 23, O = 16, H = 1 $\therefore M_r = 40$

IONIC AND COVALENT BONDING

IONIC BONDS ...
are formed between metals and non-metals when they react and ...
... are the result of electrons being completely transferred between atoms forming positive and negative ions with full outer electron shells. They are due to electrostatic forces of attraction between ions of opposite charge

eg.
Mg ATOM   O ATOM   → Mg^{2+} ION O^{2-} ION

COVALENT BONDS ...
are formed when non-metals combine together by SHARING electrons.
eg.
H H   H CL   O C O

- All these atoms have full outer electron shells, a comparison ...

IONIC COMPOUNDS	COVALENT COMPOUNDS
High mp.	Low mp and bp.
Many dissolve in water.	Do not conduct electricity.
Conduct electricity when melted or dissolved.	

STRUCTURES AND PROPERTIES OF COVALENT SUBSTANCES

- Covalent bonding can result in the formation of simple molecules (eg. hydrogen and iodine) or giant structures (eg. diamond and graphite).

SIMPLE MOLECULES ...
... have STRONG FORCES within the molecules but WEAK forces between them. They tend to have low mp's. Some are gases.

IODINE
HEAT

GASES
Nitrogen   Oxygen   Ammonia

GIANT STRUCTURES ...
... have STRONG FORCES THROUGHOUT the structure, so they tend to have high melting points.

- Diamond is a very hard crystalline solid with a very high mp.

- Graphite is layered, with strong bonds in layers but weak ones between them. It can conduct electricity.

EXOTHERMIC AND ENDOTHERMIC REACTIONS

- Chemical reactions are often accompanied by temperature changes in the reacting mixture.
- Temperature rises when energy is released during an EXOTHERMIC reaction.
- Temperature falls when energy is taken in from the surroundings during an ENDOTHERMIC reaction.
- Any type of reaction may have an accompanying temperature change ... eg. combustion, neutralisation, metal/acid etc.

BOND BREAKING AND MAKING

1. ENERGY MUST BE SUPPLIED TO BREAK CHEMICAL BONDS ...

2. ENERGY IS RELEASED WHEN CHEMICAL BONDS ARE FORMED.

ENERGY IN (ENDOTHERMIC)

(EXOTHERMIC) ENERGY OUT

ENDOTHERMIC REACTIONS
If MORE energy is NEEDED to break old bonds, than is released when new bonds are made, the reaction must be ENDOTHERMIC overall.

EXOTHERMIC REACTIONS
If MORE energy is RELEASED when new bonds are made, than is needed to break the old bonds, the reaction must be EXOTHERMIC overall.

QUANTITIES FROM EQUATIONS AND EMPIRICAL FORMULAE

MASSES OF PRODUCTS AND REACTANTS
To calculate these, we need to know ...
- the RELATIVE FORMULA MASS of the reactants and products.
- the BALANCED SYMBOL EQUATION for the reaction concerned. Substitute the first of these into the second to get a ratio of MASS OF REACTANT to MASS OF PRODUCT.

EXAMPLE - How much aluminium oxide is needed to produce 540 tonnes of aluminium?

STEP 1: Write down the equation. $2Al_2O_3 \longrightarrow 4Al + 3O_2$

STEP 2: Calculate M_r of relevant bits. $2[(2 \times 27) + (3 \times 16)] \rightarrow 4 \times 27$ Ignore the oxygen.

This is ... THE RATIO OF MASS OF REACTANT ... 204 → 108 ... TO MASS OF PRODUCT

STEP 4: Apply this ratio to the question.   If 204 tonnes of Al_2O_3 produces 108 tonnes of aluminium, ...
... then $\frac{204}{108}$ tonnes is needed to produce 1 tonne of Aluminium.
... and $\frac{204}{108} \times 540$ tonnes is needed to produce 540 tonnes of Al.
ie. 1,020 tonnes of Al_2O_3 is needed.

EMPIRICAL FORMULAE ...
represent the SIMPLEST RATIO of the ATOMS IN A COMPOUND.

STEP 1: Divide masses by A_r.   For iron $\frac{2.24}{56} = 0.04$ For oxygen $\frac{0.96}{16} = 0.06$

STEP 2: Simplify this ratio.   0.04 : 0.06 becomes 2 : 3

STEP 3: Write formula.   Simplest formula = Fe_2O_3

If you are given percentage composition values, simply use the percentage figures as if they were masses.

Speed

One way of describing the movement of an object is by measuring its **SPEED**, or how fast it is moving.

A cyclist travelling at a speed of **8** metres per second (8m/s) continuously ...

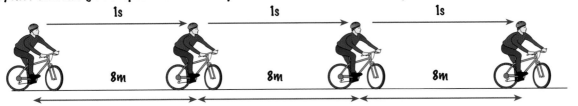

1s   1s   1s

8m   8m   8m

... would travel a **DISTANCE OF 8 METRES EVERY 1 SECOND.**

A car travelling at a speed of **60** miles per hour (60mph) continuously ...

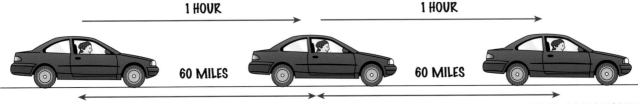

1 HOUR   1 HOUR

60 MILES   60 MILES

... would travel a **DISTANCE OF 60 MILES EVERY HOUR.**

- Speed is measured in metres per second (m/s), kilometres per hour (km/h) and miles per hour (mph).

Velocity

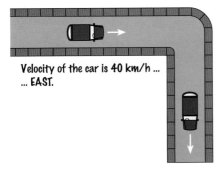

Velocity of the car is 40 km/h ...
... EAST.

Velocity of the car is now 40 km/h ...
... SOUTH.

The **VELOCITY** of a moving object is its **SPEED IN A STATED DIRECTION** ...
... ie. you know both the speed <u>and</u> the direction of travel.
This car may be travelling at a constant speed of **40 km/h** ...
... but its velocity changes because its direction of movement changes,
... ie. from **EAST** to **SOUTH**.

Distance-time Graphs

The slope or gradient of a distance-time graph is a measure of the speed of the object ...
... and the steeper the slope, the greater the speed.

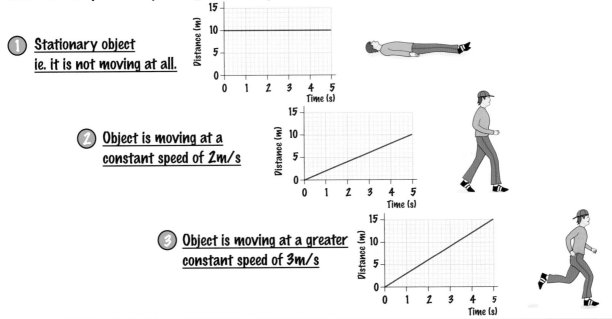

1   <u>Stationary object</u>
ie. it is not moving at all.

2   <u>Object is moving at a</u>
<u>constant speed of 2m/s</u>

3   <u>Object is moving at a greater</u>
<u>constant speed of 3m/s</u>

Measuring Acceleration

The acceleration of an object is the rate at which its velocity changes. In other words it is a measure of how quickly an object is speeding up or slowing down.

Since this cyclist INCREASES HIS VELOCITY BY 2 METRES PER SECOND EVERY 1 SECOND ...

... we can say that the ACCELERATION of the cyclist is $2m/s^2$ (2 metres per second, per second).

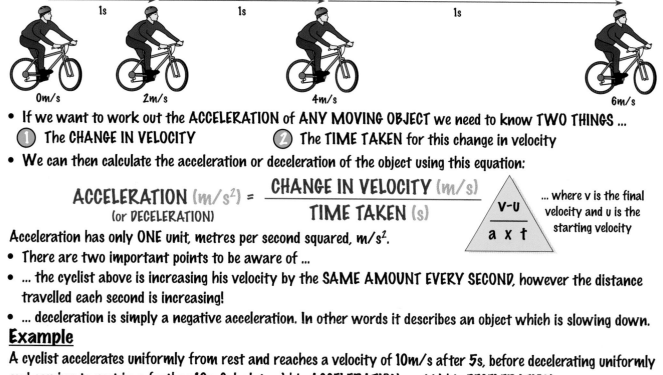

1s   1s   1s   1s

0m/s   2m/s   4m/s   6m/s

- If we want to work out the ACCELERATION of ANY MOVING OBJECT we need to know TWO THINGS ...
  ① The CHANGE IN VELOCITY   ② The TIME TAKEN for this change in velocity

- We can then calculate the acceleration or deceleration of the object using this equation:

$$\text{ACCELERATION } (m/s^2) = \frac{\text{CHANGE IN VELOCITY } (m/s)}{\text{TIME TAKEN } (s)}$$
(or DECELERATION)

$$\frac{v - u}{a \times t}$$

... where v is the final velocity and u is the starting velocity

Acceleration has only ONE unit, metres per second squared, m/s^2.

- There are two important points to be aware of ...
- ... the cyclist above is increasing his velocity by the SAME AMOUNT EVERY SECOND, however the distance travelled each second is increasing!
- ... deceleration is simply a negative acceleration. In other words it describes an object which is slowing down.

Example

A cyclist accelerates uniformly from rest and reaches a velocity of 10m/s after 5s, before decelerating uniformly and coming to rest in a further 10s. Calculate a) his ACCELERATION, and b) his DECELERATION.

a)
$$\text{ACC}^N = \frac{\text{CHANGE IN VELOCITY}}{\text{TIME TAKEN}}$$
$$= \frac{10 - 0}{5} = 2m/s^2$$

b)
$$\text{DECEL}^N = \frac{\text{CHANGE IN VELOCITY}}{\text{TIME TAKEN}}$$
$$= \frac{10 - 0}{10} = 1m/s^2$$

Speed-time Graphs

The slope or gradient of a speed-time graph is a measure of the acceleration of the object ...
... and the steeper the slope, the greater the acceleration.

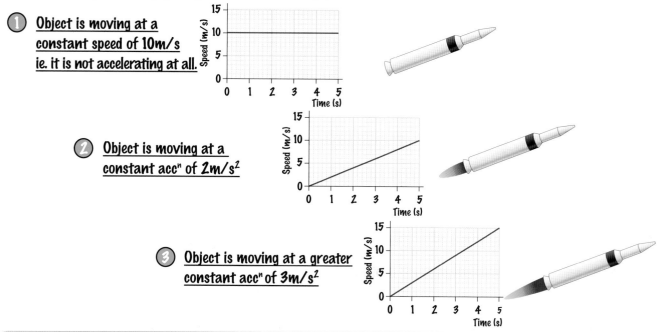

① Object is moving at a constant speed of 10m/s ie. it is not accelerating at all.

② Object is moving at a constant acc^n of $2m/s^2$

③ Object is moving at a greater constant acc^n of $3m/s^2$

Distance-time Graphs

The speed of an object can be calculated by working out the gradient of a DISTANCE-TIME GRAPH. The steeper the gradient, the faster the speed. All we have to do is take any point on the graph and read off the DISTANCE travelled at this point, and the TIME taken to get there.

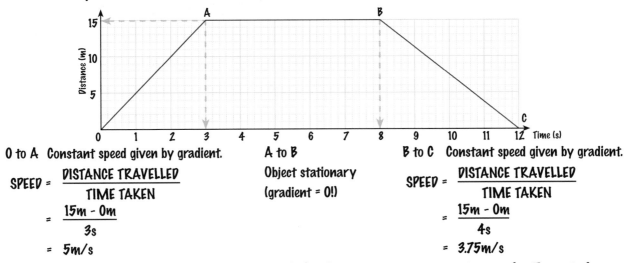

0 to A Constant speed given by gradient.

$$SPEED = \frac{DISTANCE\ TRAVELLED}{TIME\ TAKEN}$$

$$= \frac{15m - 0m}{3s}$$

$$= 5m/s$$

A to B

Object stationary (gradient = 0!)

B to C Constant speed given by gradient.

$$SPEED = \frac{DISTANCE\ TRAVELLED}{TIME\ TAKEN}$$

$$= \frac{15m - 0m}{4s}$$

$$= 3.75m/s$$

So in the example above, the object travelled at **5m/s** for **3** seconds, remained stationary for **5** secs before returning to its starting point at **3.75m/s** for **4** seconds.

Speed-time Graphs

The acceleration of an object can be calculated by working out the gradient of a SPEED-TIME GRAPH. The steeper the gradient, the greater the acceleration. All we have to do is take any point on the graph and read off the CHANGE IN SPEED over the chosen period, and the TIME taken for this change.

Example

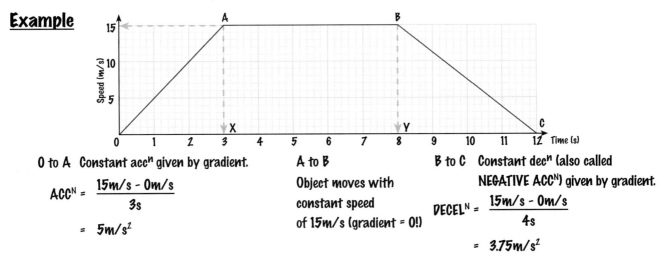

0 to A Constant acc^n given by gradient.

$$ACC^N = \frac{15m/s - 0m/s}{3s}$$

$$= 5m/s^2$$

A to B

Object moves with constant speed of 15m/s (gradient = 0!)

B to C Constant dec^n (also called NEGATIVE ACC^N) given by gradient.

$$DECEL^N = \frac{15m/s - 0m/s}{4s}$$

$$= 3.75m/s^2$$

So, in the example above, the object accelerated at **5m/s²** for **3** seconds, travelled at a constant speed of **15m/s** for **5** secs, before decelerating at a rate of **3.75m/s²** for **4** seconds.

--- HIGHER TIER ---

Also ...

The DISTANCE TRAVELLED can be calculated from the AREA BETWEEN THE CURVE (in this case a straight line) AND THE TIME AXIS. So, if we wanted to work out the total distance travelled by the object above ...

TOTAL DISTANCE TRAVELLED = AREA BETWEEN THE CURVE AND THE TIME AXIS

= Area of OAX + Area of ABYX + Area of BCY

= (½ x 3 x 15) + (5 x 15) + (½ x 4 x 15)

= 22.5 + 75 + 30

= 127.5m

Stopping Distance

The STOPPING DISTANCE of a vehicle depends on ...

... THE THINKING DISTANCE   ... THE BRAKING DISTANCE

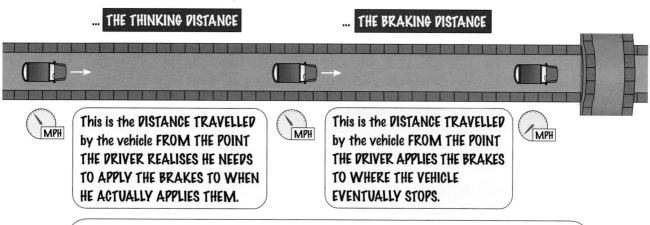

MPH

This is the DISTANCE TRAVELLED by the vehicle FROM THE POINT THE DRIVER REALISES HE NEEDS TO APPLY THE BRAKES TO WHEN HE ACTUALLY APPLIES THEM.

MPH

This is the DISTANCE TRAVELLED by the vehicle FROM THE POINT THE DRIVER APPLIES THE BRAKES TO WHERE THE VEHICLE EVENTUALLY STOPS.

MPH

STOPPING DISTANCE = THINKING DISTANCE + BRAKING DISTANCE

Factors Affecting Stopping Distance

1 The Mass Of The Vehicle

The MASS of a vehicle affects the BRAKING DISTANCE only. It has NO effect on the THINKING DISTANCE.
If the mass of the VEHICLE IS INCREASED ...

... ie. passengers, baggage etc ...

... it has greater kinetic energy ...

... which INCREASES THE BRAKING DISTANCE.

BRAKING DISTANCE

B R A K I N G   D I S T A N C E

2 The Speed Of The Vehicle

The SPEED of a vehicle affects BOTH the THINKING DISTANCE and the BRAKING DISTANCE.
This chart shows how the thinking distance and braking distance of a vehicle under normal driving conditions depends on the speed of the vehicle ...

20 MPH   6m   6m

30 MPH   9m   14m

40 MPH   12m   24m

50 MPH   15m   38m

is THINKING DISTANCE

is BRAKING DISTANCE

3 The Driver's Reaction Time

The driver's REACTION TIME ie. the time it takes from the point the driver realises he needs to apply the brakes to when he actually applies them, affects the THINKING DISTANCE only. It has no effect on the BRAKING DISTANCE.
The following would INCREASE the reaction time of the driver for obvious reasons ...

... ALCOHOL   ... DRUGS   ... TIREDNESS   ... DISTRACTIONS

FREE £££
TURN FIRST LEFT ⇧

Forces are PUSHES or PULLS eg. FRICTION, WEIGHT, AIR RESISTANCE. They are measured in NEWTONS (N) and may be different in SIZE and act in different directions. Our understanding of forces and how they affect the motion of an object has evolved over a long period of time...

- The Greek view - a force is needed to maintain the motion of an object.
- Galileo and Newton - balanced forces acting on an object cause it to continue in uniform motion in a straight line or if it is already at rest, it remains at rest.
- Newton (again) - gravitational attraction acts between all masses.

Forces Between Two Interacting Objects

Upward force exerted by ground

Downward force (WEIGHT)

Both the girl and the car ...
... exert a downward force (due to their weight) on the ground.
The ground in return ...
... exerts an upward force on the girl and car ...
... which is equal in size and opposite in direction.

In general ...
... when object A pulls or pushes object B then object B pulls or pushes object A ...
... with a force that is equal in size and opposite in direction.

How Forces Affect Movement

The movement of an object depends on the forces acting. A moving car has two forces acting on it which affects its movement ...

RESISTIVE FORCE   DRIVING FORCE

The balance of these two forces depends on whether the car is ...

① ... ACCELERATING.
When the car ACCELERATES, the DRIVING FORCE is GREATER than the RESISTIVE FORCE.
An UNBALANCED FORCE acts on the car causing it to speed up ie. accelerate.

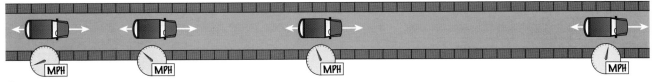

② ... BRAKING.
When the car BRAKES, the RESISTIVE FORCE is GREATER than the DRIVING FORCE.
Again, an UNBALANCED FORCE acts on the car causing it to slow down ie. decelerate.

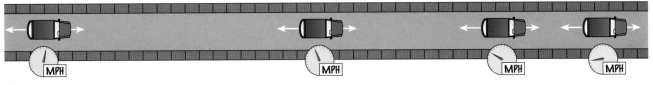

③ ... MOVING AT A CONSTANT SPEED.
When the car is moving at a CONSTANT SPEED, the DRIVING FORCE is EQUAL to the RESISTIVE FORCE.
The forces acting on the car are now BALANCED.

Force, Mass And Acceleration

If an UNBALANCED FORCE acts on an object then the acceleration of the object will depend on ...

- ... the SIZE OF THE UNBALANCED FORCE - the bigger the force, the greater the acceleration.
- ... the MASS of the object - the bigger the mass, the smaller the acceleration.

One boy pushes, exerting an UNBALANCED FORCE on the trolley ...

PUSH FORCE   1 SECOND

... causing it to move and ACCELERATE.

If two boys push the SAME trolley ...

SAME MASS   BIGGER PUSH FORCE   1 SECOND   SAME MASS

... it moves with a GREATER ACCELERATION.

However, if one boy pushes a trolley of BIGGER MASS ...

BIGGER MASS   PUSH FORCE   1 SEC   BIGGER MASS

... it moves with a SMALLER ACCELERATION.

HIGHER TIER

F = ma

Force, mass and acceleration are related by the following equation:

$$\text{FORCE (N)} = \text{MASS (kg)} \times \text{ACCELERATION (m/s}^2)$$

$$F = m \times a$$

$\dfrac{F}{m \times a}$

Examples

1. A toy car of mass 800g is accelerated by a force of 0.4N. Calculate its acceleration.

Using our equation: (rearranged using the formula triangle.)

$\dfrac{F}{m \times a}$

$$\text{ACCELERATION} = \frac{\text{FORCE}}{\text{MASS}}$$

$$= \frac{0.4\text{N}}{0.8\text{Kg}} = 0.5\text{m/s}^2$$

Mass must be in KILOGRAMS.

2. The trolley below, of mass 400kg, is pushed along a floor, with a constant speed, by one boy who exerts a push force of 150N. Another boy joins him and the push force is increased and the trolley accelerates at 0.5m/s². Calculate ... a) the force needed to achieve this acceleration and b) the total push force exerted on the trolley.

RESISTIVE FORCE 150N   CONSTANT SPEED   150N

- As the trolley is moving at a CONSTANT SPEED ...
- ... the forces acting on it must be BALANCED.
- Therefore the 150N push force must be opposed by ...
- ... an EQUAL FORCE ie. FRICTION, AIR RESISTANCE.

RESISTIVE FORCE 150N   ACCN OF 0.5m/s²   PUSH FORCE

- As the trolley is now ACCELERATING ...
- ... the push force must be GREATER than friction etc.
- These forces do not cancel each other out ...
- ... and an UNBALANCED FORCE now acts.

a) Using our equation: FORCE = MASS x ACCELERATION
                          = 400kg x 0.5m/s² = 200N

b) TOTAL 'PUSH' FORCE = FORCE TO PROVIDE ACCELERATION + FORCE NEEDED TO OVERCOME FRICTION etc.
                      = 200N + 150N = 350N

Falling objects experience TWO FORCES:

1 The DOWNWARD FORCE OF WEIGHT, W (↓) which always stays the same.

2 The UPWARD FORCE OF AIR RESISTANCE, R or DRAG (↑).

A typical falling object is a skydiver who jumps out of an aeroplane.
The speed of his descent can be considered as two separate parts ...

... BEFORE THE PARACHUTE IS OPENED

1 W

- When the skydiver jumps from the plane, he initially ACCELERATES due to the force of gravity, because the downward force due to his <u>weight (W)</u> is the only force acting on him.

2 R W

- However as he falls he experiences the frictional force of <u>air resistance (R)</u> in the opposite direction. But this isn't as great as **W** and so he continues to accelerate.

3 R W

- As his speed increases, so does the air resistance acting on him, until eventually the force due to the air resistance is equal to the force due to his weight.

4 R W
This means that the resultant force acting on him is now zero and he continues to fall at a constant speed called the TERMINAL VELOCITY.

BALANCED FORCES AND THEREFORE CONSTANT SPEED →

5 R W

... AFTER THE PARACHUTE IS OPENED

- When the parachute is opened unbalanced forces act again because the upward force of **R** is now greatly increased and is bigger than **W**. This decreases his speed and as his speed decreases so does **R**.

6 R W

7 R W

- Eventually R decreases until it is equal to **W**. The forces acting are once again balanced and for the second time he falls at a steady speed, slower than before though ie. a new terminal velocity.

8

Graph: SPEED OF SKYDIVER (vertical axis) vs TIME (horizontal axis)

- **1** ... **2** SPEED INCREASES ... **3** ... **4** STEADY SPEED
- BEFORE | AFTER
- **5** SPEED DECREASES ... **6** ... **7** STEADY SPEED **8**

NB

In the absence of air resistance ALL falling bodies accelerate at the same rate. If you were to drop a feather and a hammer, from the same height at the same time on the Moon BOTH would reach the surface simultaneously.

Work

- When a FORCE MOVES an OBJECT ...
- ... WORK is DONE ON THE OBJECT resulting in the TRANSFER OF ENERGY where ...

WORK DONE (J) = ENERGY TRANSFERRED (J)

Work done, force and distance moved are related by the equation:

WORK DONE (J) = FORCE APPLIED (N) x DISTANCE MOVED IN DIRECTION OF FORCE (m)

$$W = F \times d$$

Example

A man pushes a car with a steady force of 250N.
The car moves a distance of 20m. How much work does he do?

250N PUSH

Using the equation: WORK DONE = FORCE APPLIED x DISTANCE MOVED IN DIRECTION OF FORCE

= 250N x 20m

= 5,000J (or 5KJ)

Power

- POWER is the RATE of DOING WORK or the RATE of TRANSFER OF ENERGY.
- The GREATER the POWER, the MORE WORK is DONE EVERY SECOND.
- Power is measured in watts (W) or joules per second (J/s).

If two boys, Tom and Jim ...
... of the SAME WEIGHT ...
... race up the SAME HILL ...
... they both do the SAME AMOUNT ...
... of WORK to reach the top.

However ...
... since Tom has done the same amount of work as Jim but in a shorter time, then Tom has a GREATER POWER.

Power, work done and time taken are related by the equation:

$$\text{POWER (W or J/s)} = \frac{\text{WORK DONE (J)}}{\text{TIME TAKEN (s)}}$$

$$P = \frac{W}{t}$$

Example

A crane lifts a load of 20,000N through a distance of 10m in 4s. Calculate the output power of the crane.
FIRSTLY WE NEED TO WORK OUT HOW MUCH WORK THE CRANE DOES AGAINST GRAVITY.

Using the equation: WORK DONE = FORCE APP. x DIST. MOVED

= 20,000N x 10m

= 200,000J

THE LOAD HAS NOW GAINED THIS AMOUNT OF ENERGY

20,000 N

10m

Using the equation: POWER = $\frac{\text{WORK DONE}}{\text{TIME TAKE}}$

= $\frac{200,000J}{4s}$

= 50,000 W (or J/s)

or P = 50 kW ... SINCE 1kW = 1,000W

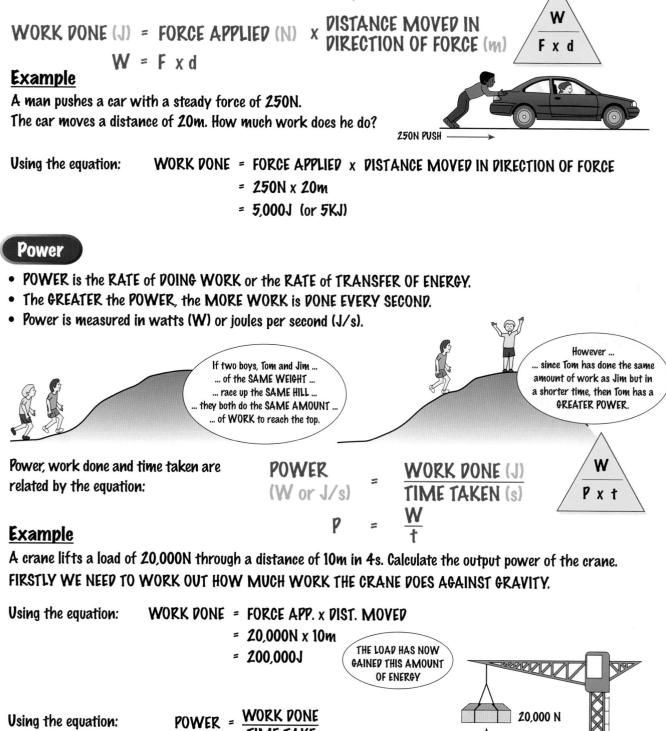

Gravitational Potential Energy

This is the ENERGY STORED in an object due to its position.
If an object can fall it's got GRAVITATIONAL POTENTIAL ENERGY.
A swimmer on a diving board has gravitational potential energy.

Kinetic Energy

This is the ENERGY an object has because of its MOVEMENT.
If its MOVING, it's got KINETIC ENERGY.
A moving car has kinetic energy.

NB When the swimmer jumps off the diving board above there will be a transfer of energy ...
... from GRAVITATIONAL POTENTIAL ENERGY TO KINETIC ENERGY.

───── HIGHER TIER ─────

The Equations

① Gravitational Potential Energy

$$\text{GRAVITATIONAL POTENTIAL ENERGY (J)} = \text{MASS (kg)} \times \text{GRAVITATIONAL FIELD STRENGTH (N/kg)} \times \text{VERTICAL HEIGHT (m)}$$

$$GPE = m \times g \times h$$

GRAVITATIONAL FIELD STRENGTH, g, is a constant and has a value of 10N/kg.
All this means is that EVERY 1kg OF MATTER near the surface of the Earth
experiences a DOWNWARDS FORCE of 10N due to gravity.

$$\frac{GPE}{m \times g \times h}$$

Example

A skier of mass 80kg takes the ski lift which takes him from a height of 1000m to a height
of 3000m above ground. By how much does his gravitational potential energy increase?
Using the equation:

$$\text{GRAVITATIONAL POTENTIAL ENERGY (J)} = \text{MASS (kg)} \times \text{GRAVITATIONAL FIELD STRENGTH (N/kg)} \times \text{VERTICAL HEIGHT (m)}$$

$$= 80kg \times 10N/kg \times (3000m - 1000m)$$
$$= 80kg \times 10N/kg \times 2000m$$
$$= 1,600,000J$$

The skier was already at a height of 1000m above ground

② Kinetic Energy

$$\text{KINETIC ENERGY (J)} = \frac{1}{2} \times \text{MASS (kg)} \times \text{VELOCITY}^2 \text{ (m/s)}^2$$

$$KE = \frac{1}{2} \times m \times v^2$$

$$\frac{KE}{\frac{1}{2} \times m \times v^2}$$

Example

A car of mass 1000kg is moving at a speed of 10m/s. How much kinetic energy does it have?
Using the equation:

$$\text{KINETIC ENERGY (J)} = \frac{1}{2} \times \text{MASS (kg)} \times \text{VELOCITY}^2 \text{ (m/s)}^2$$

$$= \frac{1}{2} \times 1000kg \times 10^2 \text{ (m/s)}^2$$

$$= 50,000J$$

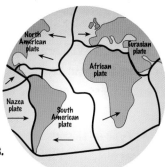

Movement Of The Lithosphere

The Earth's LITHOSPHERE ie. the CRUST and the UPPER PART OF THE MANTLE ...

... is 'cracked' into several large pieces called TECTONIC PLATES.

These plates move slowly, at speeds of a few cm per year, ...

... driven by CONVECTION CURRENTS in the MANTLE, ...

... which are caused by HEAT released by RADIOACTIVE DECAY.

Plate tectonic processes result in the formation, deformation and recycling of rocks.

Three Things That Can Happen

The 'plates' above can basically only do THREE things:

① Slide Past Each Other

When plates SLIDE, HUGE STRESSES AND STRAINS build up in the crust ...

... which eventually have to be RELEASED in order for MOVEMENT to occur.

This 'release' of energy results in an EARTHQUAKE. A classic example of
this is the West Coast of North America (esp. California).

② Move Away From Each Other – Constructive Plate Boundaries

When plates MOVE AWAY FROM EACH OTHER, at an oceanic ridge, FRACTURES OCCUR, ...

... these are filled by MAGMA to produce NEW BASALTIC OCEAN CRUST, ...

... at a rate of 2cm per year.

This is known as SEA FLOOR SPREADING, and undersea volcanoes occur here.

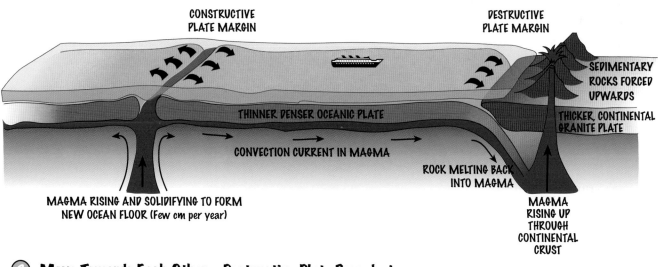

CONSTRUCTIVE PLATE MARGIN

DESTRUCTIVE PLATE MARGIN

SEDIMENTARY ROCKS FORCED UPWARDS

THINNER DENSER OCEANIC PLATE

THICKER, CONTINENTAL GRANITE PLATE

CONVECTION CURRENT IN MAGMA

ROCK MELTING BACK INTO MAGMA

MAGMA RISING AND SOLIDIFYING TO FORM NEW OCEAN FLOOR (Few cm per year)

MAGMA RISING UP THROUGH CONTINENTAL CRUST

③ Move Towards Each Other – Destructive Plate Boundaries

As plates are moving away from each other in some places ...

... it follows that they must be MOVING TOWARDS EACH OTHER in other places.

This always results in the THINNER, DENSER, OCEANIC PLATE being FORCED DOWN (SUBDUCTED) ...

... into the MANTLE beneath the THICKER CONTINENTAL GRANITE PLATE where it partially MELTS.

This subduction forces continental crust to be compressed resulting in folding and metamorphism.

EARTHQUAKES are common and even VOLCANOES are formed ...

... due to magma rising up through the continental crust.

Effects Of Seismic Waves

SEISMIC WAVES are shock waves of great energy that travel through the Earth. They are caused by EARTHQUAKES or 'underground explosions' and are detected on the Earth's surface using seismographs. When seismic waves reach the surface of the Earth they can cause massive destruction to buildings etc.

One type of seismic wave makes buildings VIBRATE UP AND DOWN.

SEISMIC WAVES

Another type of seismic wave makes buildings VIBRATE FROM LEFT TO RIGHT.

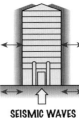

SEISMIC WAVES

◄ HIGHER TIER ◄

Evidence For The Earth's Structure

Although seismic waves can cause massive destruction the paths they follow and their speed of travel have been instrumental in providing evidence that the EARTH has a LAYERED STRUCTURE. When an earthquake occurs there are two types of seismic wave generated ...

PRIMARY WAVES (P waves) ...

- ... are LONGITUDINAL WAVES where the ground is made to VIBRATE in the SAME DIRECTION as the seismic wave is travelling ie. UP and DOWN.
- ... CAN TRAVEL THROUGH BOTH SOLID AND LIQUID.
- ... CAN TRAVEL THROUGH ALL LAYERS OF THE EARTH.
- are FASTER THAN S WAVES.

SECONDARY WAVES (S waves) ...

- ... are TRANSVERSE WAVES where the ground is made to VIBRATE at RIGHT ANGLES to the DIRECTION the seismic wave is travelling ie. from LEFT to RIGHT.
- ... CAN TRAVEL THROUGH A SOLID BUT NOT A LIQUID.
- ... CANNOT TRAVEL THROUGH THE OUTER CORE.
- are SLOWER THAN P WAVES.

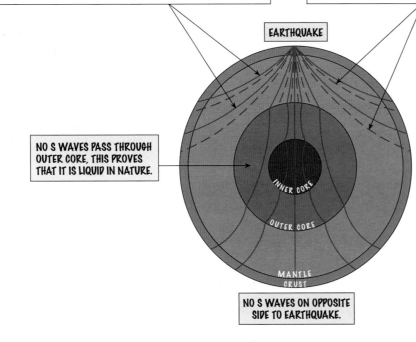

EARTHQUAKE

NO S WAVES PASS THROUGH OUTER CORE, THIS PROVES THAT IT IS LIQUID IN NATURE.

INNER CORE

OUTER CORE

MANTLE
CRUST

NO S WAVES ON OPPOSITE SIDE TO EARTHQUAKE.

The study of these seismic waves suggests that the EARTH is made up of ...
- A THIN CRUST.
- A MANTLE which is SEMI-FLUID and extends almost HALFWAY TO THE CENTRE.
- A CORE which is over HALF of the Earth's DIAMETER with a LIQUID OUTER PART and a SOLID INNER PART.

Activity Of A Radioactive Isotope

Radioactive isotopes are atoms with unstable nuclei which may disintegrate or decay emitting radiation.
The ACTIVITY of a radioactive isotope is the AVERAGE NUMBER of DISINTEGRATIONS that occur EVERY SECOND.
It is measured in BECQUERELS and decreases over a period of time ...

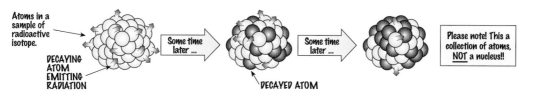

This idea can be used to DATE CERTAIN MATERIALS by MEASURING the AMOUNT OF RADIATION THEY EMIT ...
... eg.   • Very old samples of wood ...   • Remains of prehistoric bones ...   • Certain types of rock.

Half-life

This is the TIME it takes for HALF THE UNDECAYED NUCLEI TO DECAY.

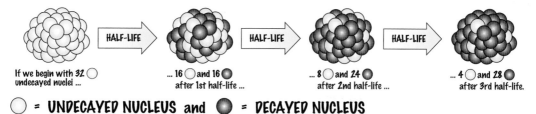

If we begin with 32 ◯ undecayed nuclei ...   ... 16 ◯ and 16 ● after 1st half-life ...   ... 8 ◯ and 24 ● after 2nd half-life ...   ... 4 ◯ and 28 ● after 3rd half-life.

◯ = UNDECAYED NUCLEUS and ● = DECAYED NUCLEUS

If the isotope has a very long half-life then it remains active for a very long time. This is why radioactive waste
has to be immobilised ie. changed into a form that limits the likelihood of the radioactive isotopes escaping into
the environment.

Calculations Involving Half-life

Certain materials contain radioactive isotopes which decay to produce stable isotopes. If we know the 'PROPORTION'
of each of these isotopes and the HALF-LIFE of the radioactive isotope then it is possible to date the material.
- IGNEOUS ROCKS may contain URANIUM isotopes which decay via a series of relatively short-lived isotopes
  to produce stable isotopes of LEAD. This takes ages because uranium has a VERY LONG HALF-LIFE.
- WOOD and BONES contain the CARBON-14 isotope which decays when the organism dies!

Example 1

A very small sample of dead wood has an activity of 1000 becquerels over a period of time. The same mass
of 'live' wood has an activity of 4000 becquerels over an identical time period. If the half-life of carbon-14
is 5,600 years, calculate the age of the wood.

original activity **4000** $\xrightarrow{\text{HALF-LIFE}}$ **2000** $\xrightarrow{\text{HALF-LIFE}}$ **1000** present activity

Therefore the carbon-14 has taken 2 x HALF-LIVES to DECAY TO ITS PRESENT ACTIVITY.

Age of wood = 2 x 5,600 years = <u>11,200 years</u>

Example 2

A sample of igneous rock is found to contain three times as much lead compared to uranium.
If the half-life of uranium is 700,000,000 years, calculate the age of the rock.
Fraction of lead present is $\frac{3}{4}$ while that of uranium is $\frac{1}{4}$ (There is 3 x as much lead as uranium remember!)
Frac^n of lead now present + Frac^n of uranium now present = Orig. amount of uranium present = $\frac{3}{4} + \frac{1}{4}$ = 1

Original amount of uranium decays. **1** $\xrightarrow{\text{HALF-LIFE}}$ $\frac{1}{2}$ $\xrightarrow{\text{HALF-LIFE}}$ $\frac{1}{4}$ Final amount of uranium now present

Age of rock = 2 x HALF-LIFE = 2 x 700,000,000 years = <u>1,400,000,000 years</u>

SPEED AND VELOCITY

- Speed can be measured in m/s, km/h or mph.
- VELOCITY is speed in a stated direction ...
  ... ie. you know both the speed and direction of travel.
- Speed can be shown on a DISTANCE-TIME graph.

STATIONARY OBJECT   CONSTANT SPEED OF 2m/s   CONSTANT SPEED OF 3m/s

INTERPRETING DISTANCE-TIME GRAPHS

Stationary

5 m/s away from the starting position

3.75 m/s back to the starting position

The GRADIENT (slope) of a distance-time graph gives the SPEED of the object.

ACCELERATION

Acceleration is the rate at which the velocity of an object changes.

$$\text{ACCELERATION (m/s}^2) = \frac{\text{CHANGE IN VELOCITY (m/s)}}{\text{TIME TAKEN (s)}}$$

It is only measured in metres per second per second (m/s^2).
Acceleration can be shown on a SPEED-TIME graph.

$$\frac{v - u}{a \times t}$$

CONSTANT SPEED   CONSTANT ACCELERATION OF 2m/s^2 CONSTANT ACCELERATION OF 3m/s^2

INTERPRETING SPEED-TIME GRAPHS

Constant Speed

Acceleration of 5 m/s^2

Deceleration of 3.75 m/s^2

The GRADIENT (slope) of a speed-time graph gives the acceleration of the object.

The AREA between the curve and the time axis represents the DISTANCE TRAVELLED by the object.

FORCE, MASS AND ACCELERATION

FORCES

- A force is a PUSH or a PULL measured in NEWTONS (N).
  - The car exerts a downward force on the ground.
  - The ground in return exerts an upward force on the car ...
  ... which is equal in size and opposite in direction.
- A moving car has two forces acting on it which affect its movement ... RESISTIVE FORCE   DRIVING FORCE
- If DRIVING FORCE > RESISTIVE FORCE ... car accelerates.
- If RESISTIVE FORCE > DRIVING FORCE ... car decelerates.
- If DRIVING FORCE = RESISTIVE FORCE ... car moves at a constant speed.

FORCE, MASS AND ACCELERATION

- When an UNBALANCED FORCE acts on an object, the acceleration of the object depends on ...
- ... the SIZE OF THE UNBALANCED FORCE - the bigger the force, the greater the acceleration.
- ... the MASS OF THE OBJECT - the bigger the mass, the smaller the acceleration.

F = ma
FORCE (N) = MASS (kg) x ACCELERATION (m/s^2)

$$\frac{F}{m \times a}$$

- If an object is moving at a CONSTANT SPEED the forces acting on it are BALANCED.

STOPPING DISTANCE AND TERMINAL VELOCITY

STOPPING DISTANCE depends on ...

- The THINKING DISTANCE and the BRAKING DISTANCE.
- STOPPING DISTANCE = THINKING DISTANCE + BRAKING DISTANCE.
- The MASS of a vehicle affects the BRAKING DISTANCE only.
- The SPEED of a vehicle affects both the THINKING DISTANCE ...
  ... and the BRAKING DISTANCE.
- The driver's REACTION TIME affects the THINKING DISTANCE only.

TERMINAL VELOCITY A skydiver ...

... experiences acceleration due to gravity ...

... followed by steadily increasing air resistance which causes ...

... a decrease in the RATE OF ACCELERATION until ...

... when R=W he reaches TERMINAL VELOCITY and falls at a constant speed.

- In the absence of air resistance, all falling bodies accelerate at the same rate.

WORK, POWER AND ENERGY

- WORK DONE (J) = ENERGY TRANSFERRED (J)
- WORK DONE (J) = FORCE APPLIED (N) x DISTANCE MOVED (m)
- $$\text{POWER (W)} = \frac{\text{WORK DONE (J)}}{\text{TIME TAKEN (s)}}$$

The unit of power is the watt or joule per second.

GRAVITATIONAL POTENTIAL ENERGY ...

- ... is the energy stored in an object due to its position.

KINETIC ENERGY ...

- ... is the energy an object has because of its movement.

THE EQUATIONS

GRAVITATIONAL POT. ENERGY (J) = MASS (kg) x GRAVITATIONAL FIELD STRENGTH (N/kg) x VERTICAL HEIGHT (m)

- GRAVITATIONAL FIELD STRENGTH is a constant and has a value of 10N/kg here on Earth.

$$\frac{GPE}{m \times g \times h}$$

KINETIC ENERGY (J) = $\frac{1}{2}$ x MASS (kg) x VELOCITY^2 (m/s)^2

$$\frac{KE}{\frac{1}{2} \times m \times v^2}$$

SEISMIC WAVES, PLATE TECTONICS AND HALF-LIFE

SEISMIC WAVES ... are shock waves created by earthquakes or 'underground explosions'.

PRIMARY WAVES (P waves)
- ... are LONGITUDINAL WAVES where the ground is made to VIBRATE in the SAME DIRECTION as the seismic wave is travelling ie. UP and DOWN.
- ... CAN TRAVEL THROUGH BOTH SOLID AND LIQUID.
- ... CAN TRAVEL THROUGH ALL LAYERS OF THE EARTH.
- ... are FASTER THAN S WAVES.

SECONDARY WAVES (S waves)
- ... are TRANSVERSE WAVES where the ground is made to VIBRATE at RIGHT ANGLES to the DIRECTION the seismic wave is travelling ie. from LEFT to RIGHT.
- ... CAN TRAVEL THROUGH A SOLID BUT NOT A LIQUID.
- ... CANNOT TRAVEL THROUGH THE OUTER CORE.
- ... are SLOWER THAN P WAVES.

PLATE TECTONICS ... The LITHOSPHERE is 'cracked' into several large pieces called TECTONIC PLATES. These plates can ... a) Slide past each other.
b) Move away from each other - constructive plate boundaries.
c) Move towards each other - destructive plate boundaries.

a)   b)   c)

HALF-LIFE

- The ACTIVITY of a radioactive isotope is the average number of disintegrations that occur every second. Measured in BECQUERELS.
- HALF-LIFE is the time it takes for half the undecayed nuclei to decay.
- Can be used to date certain materials.

'Generating' Static Electricity

Materials that allow electricity to flow through them easily are called ELECTRICAL CONDUCTORS.
METALS are good conductors. PLASTICS and many other materials, on the other hand, do not allow electricity to flow through them; they are called INSULATORS.

It is possible though for an insulator to become ELECTRICALLY CHARGED if there is friction between it and another insulator. When this happens there is a transfer of electrons from one material to the other. They are now charged with STATIC ELECTRICITY which means that the electricity stays on the material and doesn't move.

You can 'generate' static electricity by rubbing a balloon against a jumper.

The electrically charged balloon will then attract very small objects.

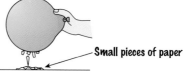

Small pieces of paper

- Electric charge (static) builds up when ELECTRONS (which have a NEGATIVE charge) are 'rubbed off' one material onto another. The material receiving electrons becomes NEGATIVELY CHARGED and the one giving up electrons becomes EQUALLY POSITIVELY CHARGED.

eg. PERSPEX ROD RUBBED WITH A CLOTH

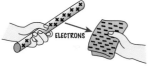

ELECTRONS

eg. EBONITE ROD RUBBED WITH FUR

ELECTRONS

Perspex LOSES electrons ...	Cloth GAINS electrons ...	Ebonite GAINS electrons ...	Fur LOSES electrons ...
... to become ...	... to become ...	... to become ...	... to become ...
... POSITIVELY CHARGED.	... NEGATIVELY CHARGED.	... NEGATIVELY CHARGED.	... POSITIVELY CHARGED.

Repulsion And Attraction Between Charged Materials

Very simply, two materials with ...

... THE SAME CHARGES REPEL EACH OTHER.

NB
We would get the same with two ebonite rods.

- The SUSPENDED PERSPEX ROD ...
- ... is REPELLED by the OTHER PERSPEX ROD.

... DIFFERENT CHARGES ATTRACT EACH OTHER.

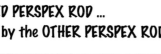

NB
We would get the same if the rods were the other way around.

- The SUSPENDED PERSPEX ROD ...
- ... is ATTRACTED by the EBONITE ROD.

Common Electrostatic Phenomena

The following all involve the movement of ELECTRONS ...

1 ... LIGHTNING

2 ... CHARGES ON SYNTHETIC FABRICS

3 ... SHOCKS FROM CAR DOORS

Clouds become charged up by rising hot air until discharge occurs ie. a bolt of lightning.

'Static' sparks when synthetic clothing is removed from body.

A car can become charged up due to friction between itself and air when it moves.

Using Static In Everyday Life

1. THE PHOTOCOPIER

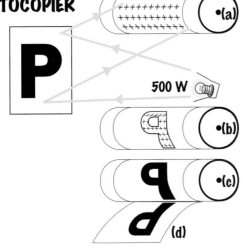

(a) A copying plate is electrically charged (usually positive). An image of the page to be copied is projected onto the plate.

(b) Light causes charge to leak away leaving an 'electrostatic impression' of the page.

(c) This charged impression of the plate attracts tiny specks of black powder.

(d) This powder is then transferred from the plate to paper which is heated to fix the final image.

2. INKJET PRINTER

Negatively charged ink droplets are squirted between two oppositely charged metal plates across which a variable voltage is applied enabling the charges to be varied and swapped very quickly. The charged droplets of ink are attracted towards the plate with the opposite charge and are therefore deflected to their precise vertical location on the page, while the carriage of the printer moves horizontally across the paper, to give a full range of ink projection.

NB This is now old technology but the principle is still important. Also, the system would work just as well with positively charged ink droplets.

Fine nozzle producing negatively charged droplets.

INK JET PRINTERS
The technology involved in these machines enabling users to print cheaply
PRINCIPLES IN
high quality

Discharging Unsafe Static

FILLING AIRCRAFT FUEL TANKS

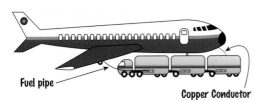

Fuel pipe

Copper Conductor

During refuelling the fuel gains electrons from the fuel pipe, making the pipe positively charged and the fuel negatively charged. The resulting voltage between the two can cause a spark (DISCHARGE). You can imagine the rest!!!

To solve the problem the fuel tank can be earthed using a copper conductor or the tanker and the plane can be linked by a copper conductor.

---- HIGHER TIER ----

Earthing

Doing the above allows a constant safe discharge to occur resulting in the equalisation of the electron imbalance between the two bodies. When earthing occurs it is always ELECTRONS that flow from one body to the other to remove the imbalance ...

Negatively charged dome

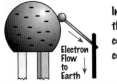

Electron Flow to Earth

In this case electrons flow from the dome to Earth via the conductor ... until the dome is completely discharged.

Positively charged dome

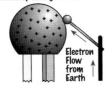

Electron Flow from Earth

This time the electrons flow from Earth to cancel out the positive charge on the dome ... until the dome is completely discharged.

Charge

An electric current is the rate of flow of charge which transfers energy from a battery or power supply to the components in the circuit.

The amount of electrical CHARGE which passes ANY POINT in a circuit is measured in coulombs (C) and depends on ...
... the CURRENT that flows and the TIME for which the current flows.

Charge, current and time are related by the equation:

$$\text{CHARGE (C)} = \text{CURRENT (A)} \times \text{TIME (s)}$$
$$Q = I \times t$$

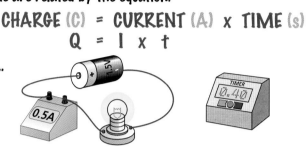 (Q represents charge)

Here is a simple circuit ...

If the circuit above is switched on for 40 seconds and a current of 0.5 amps flows, then ...

... using the equation: CHARGE = CURRENT x TIME

= 0.5A x 40s

= 20 coulombs

This AMOUNT OF CHARGE goes past any POINT in the circuit in the 40 SECONDS.

Electrical Power

From above, when charge flows through a component an ENERGY TRANSFER TAKES PLACE. The RATE of this ENERGY TRANSFER is the ELECTRICAL POWER of the component or appliance and is measured in joules/second or WATTS (W) where 1 watt is the transfer of 1 joule of energy in 1 second.

Electrical power is calculated using the following equation:

$$\text{ELECTRICAL POWER (W)} = \text{CURRENT (A)} \times \text{VOLTAGE (V)}$$
$$P = I \times V$$

Most appliances have a rating plate on them which gives us their maximum power and their working voltage. We can then calculate the current passing through the appliance, for example ...

POWER   VOLTAGE

900W   230V-50Hz
WELLMAN
SUPERSTEAM
SERIAL No 6161623PW

DOMESTIC IRON RATING PLATE

Using our equation:
(rearranged using triangle)

$$\text{CURRENT} = \frac{\text{ELECTRICAL POWER}}{\text{VOLTAGE}}$$

$$= \frac{900W}{230V}$$

$$= 3.9 \text{ amps.}$$

Not all appliances though have the same electrical power. Here are four typical appliances ...

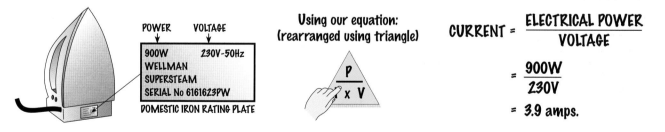

APPLIANCE				
ELECTRICAL POWER (W)	115 W	600 W	1100 W	2000 W
VOLTAGE (V)	230 V	230 V	230 V	230 V
CURRENT (A)	0.5 A	2.6 A	4.8 A	8.7 A

Electric Current In Metals

In METALS an electric current is <u>only</u> a flow of NEGATIVELY CHARGED ELECTRONS.
A very common source of electrons is a battery. Here is a very simple circuit ...

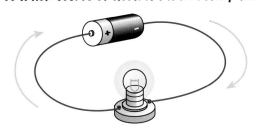

Direction of electron flow

The electrons flow from the NEGATIVE (-) terminal of the battery through the circuit to the POSITIVE (+) terminal.

Electric Current In Molten And Dissolved Electrolytes

Some chemical compounds will allow an electric current to flow through them when they are MOLTEN
or DISSOLVED IN WATER.

These electrolytes contain NEGATIVE and POSITIVE IONS ...

... and the electric current is due to <u>both</u> ...

... NEGATIVELY CHARGED IONS MOVING TO THE POSITIVE ELECTRODE ...

... and POSITIVELY CHARGED IONS MOVING TO THE NEGATIVE ELECTRODE.

When this happens SIMPLE SUBSTANCES are released at the <u>TWO ELECTRODES</u>.

In the electrolysis of copper chloride solution
the simple substances released are COPPER
and CHLORINE GAS.

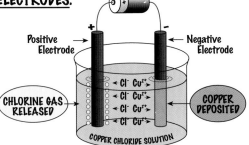

Positive Electrode   Negative Electrode

CHLORINE GAS RELEASED   COPPER DEPOSITED

COPPER CHLORIDE SOLUTION

Energy Transferred

The amount of ENERGY TRANSFERRED to a component or appliance is given by the relationship ...

ENERGY TRANSFERRED (J) = CURRENT (A) x VOLTAGE (V) x TIME (s)

$$E = I \times V \times t$$

$$\frac{E}{I \times V \times t}$$

Here is a simple circuit ...

0.6A   TIMER 0:30

If the circuit above is switched on for 30 seconds, then ...

Using the relationship: ENERGY TRANSFERRED = CURRENT x VOLTAGE x TIME
                                            =   0.6A   x   1.5V   x   30s
                                            =   27J

This amount of electrical energy is transferred by the bulb into other forms of energy
ie. light and heat, during the 30 seconds.

Voltage

VOLTAGE is the ENERGY TRANSFERRED PER UNIT CHARGE PASSED. The battery in the circuit above has a voltage
of 1.5V which means that for EVERY 1 COULOMB OF CHARGE that passes through the bulb,
1.5 JOULES OF ELECTRICAL ENERGY IS TRANSFERRED into OTHER FORMS OF ENERGY.

Consequently voltage can also be measured in JOULES PER COULOMB.

Electromagnetism

If an ELECTRIC CURRENT flows through a wire a MAGNETIC FIELD is formed around the wire creating an electromagnet. This is a magnet that can be switched on and off.
The magnetic field lines produced are circular; reversing the current reverses the direction of the field.

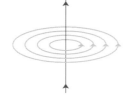
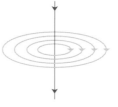

The Principle Of The Motor Effect

When a wire carrying an ELECTRIC CURRENT (as above) ...
... is placed in a PERMANENT MAGNETIC FIELD, the magnetic field formed around the wire interacts ...
... with the permanent magnetic field causing the wire to experience a force which causes it to move.
Reversing the direction of flow of the current, reverses the direction of the force acting on the wire.

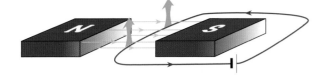
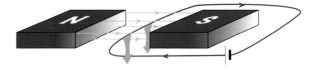

The Direct Current (d.c.) Motor

Electric motors form the basis of a vast range of electrical devices both in and out of the home.
These rely on the principle of the motor effect.

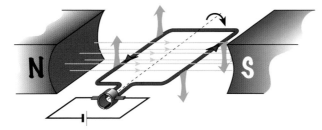

As a current flows through the coil a MAGNETIC FIELD is formed around the coil...
... creating an ELECTROMAGNET.
This magnetic field INTERACTS with the PERMANENT MAGNETIC FIELD...
... which exists between the TWO POLES, N and S.

OPPOSITE FORCES act on each side of the coil, causing the coil to ROTATE ...
... to give us a very simple motor.
The force acting is always PERPENDICULAR ie. at 90° to both the WIRE CARRYING THE CURRENT and the MAGNETIC FIELD.

If we take ...
... the LEFT-HAND SIDE OF THE COIL.   ... the RIGHT-HAND SIDE OF THE COIL.

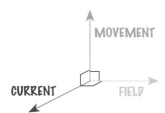
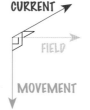

Distributing Electricity

Electricity generated at POWER STATIONS is distributed to homes, schools, shops, factories etc. all over the country by a network of cables called the NATIONAL GRID. Transformers are used to change the voltage of an a.c. supply, and are used both before and after transmission through the grid.

- Before transmission onto the GRID ...
  - ... TRANSFORMERS are used to 'STEP-UP'...
    - ... the VOLTAGE of the electricity generated.
- Before consumption by homes, schools etc. ...
  - ... LOCAL TRANSFORMERS are used to 'STEP-DOWN' ...
    - ... the voltage to a level which is safe to use.

Reducing The Energy Loss During Transmission

The HIGHER the CURRENT that passes through ANY WIRE the greater the AMOUNT OF ENERGY LOST AS HEAT FROM THE WIRE. So we need to transmit as low a current as possible through the POWER LINES.

But since, ELECTRICAL POWER = CURRENT x VOLTAGE

... the smaller the current, the higher the voltage needed to transmit energy at the same rate!
This is where transformers come in.

Low voltage, high current for domestic consumption.

STEP-UP TRANSFORMER FOR TRANSMISSION

STEP-DOWN TRANSFORMER FOR CONSUMPTION

High voltage, low current, small energy loss as heat during transmission.

How Transformers Work

Transformers consist of ...
- Two COILS called the PRIMARY (INPUT) COIL and the SECONDARY (OUTPUT) COIL wrapped around a SOFT IRON CORE.
- These coils have a different number of turns.

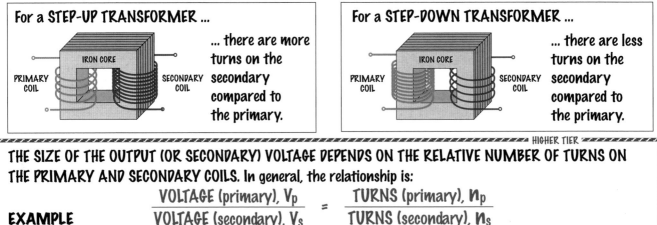

For a STEP-UP TRANSFORMER ...

IRON CORE

PRIMARY COIL

SECONDARY COIL

... there are more turns on the secondary compared to the primary.

For a STEP-DOWN TRANSFORMER ...

IRON CORE

PRIMARY COIL

SECONDARY COIL

... there are less turns on the secondary compared to the primary.

━━ HIGHER TIER ━━

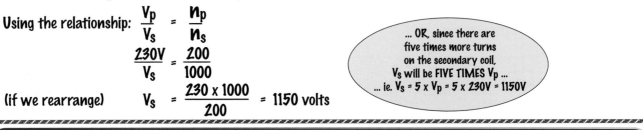

THE SIZE OF THE OUTPUT (OR SECONDARY) VOLTAGE DEPENDS ON THE RELATIVE NUMBER OF TURNS ON THE PRIMARY AND SECONDARY COILS. In general, the relationship is:

$$\frac{\text{VOLTAGE (primary), } V_p}{\text{VOLTAGE (secondary), } V_s} = \frac{\text{TURNS (primary), } n_p}{\text{TURNS (secondary), } n_s}$$

EXAMPLE

A voltage of 230V is applied to the primary coil which has 200 turns. The secondary coil has 1000 turns. What is the voltage across the secondary coil?

Using the relationship: $\frac{V_p}{V_s} = \frac{n_p}{n_s}$

$$\frac{230V}{V_s} = \frac{200}{1000}$$

(if we rearrange) $V_s = \frac{230 \times 1000}{200} = 1150 \text{ volts}$

... OR, since there are five times more turns on the secondary coil, V_s will be FIVE TIMES V_p ...
... ie. $V_s = 5 \times V_p = 5 \times 230V = 1150V$

Waves are a regular pattern of disturbance that transfer energy and information from one point to another without any transfer of matter.

The Wave Equation – Applies To All Waves

For any wave the WAVE SPEED, FREQUENCY and WAVELENGTH are related by the equation:

$$\text{WAVE SPEED (m/s)} = \text{FREQUENCY (Hz)} \times \text{WAVELENGTH (m)}$$
$$v = f \times \lambda$$

EXAMPLE 1

A sound wave has a frequency of 168Hz and a wavelength of 2m, what is the speed of sound?

Using our equation: Wave speed = Frequency × Wavelength

$$v = 168\text{Hz} \times 2\text{m}$$
$$= \underline{336\text{m/s}}$$

EXAMPLE 2

Radio 5 Live transmits from London on a frequency of 909 kHz. If the speed of radio waves is 300,000,000m/s, what is the wavelength of the waves?

Using our equation: (now rearranged)

$$\text{Wavelength} = \frac{\text{Wave speed}}{\text{Frequency}}$$

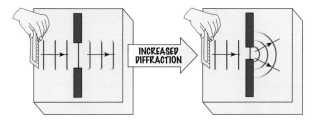

$$= \frac{300,000,000\text{m/s}}{909,000\text{Hz}} = \underline{330\text{m}}$$

Diffraction Of Waves

• When WAVES MOVE THROUGH A GAP or PAST AN OBSTACLE ...

• ... they SPREAD OUT FROM THE EDGES. This is DIFFRACTION.

Diffraction is most obvious when:

1. THE SIZE OF THE GAP IS SIMILAR TO THE WAVELENGTH OF THE WAVES.	2. THE WAVES WHICH PASS OBSTACLES HAVE LONG WAVELENGTHS.

Examples of diffraction ...

• Water waves are diffracted by harbours.

• Light is diffracted by a single narrow slit.

• Sound is diffracted by large buildings and doorways.

The fact that both light and sound can be diffracted provides evidence that they travel as waves.

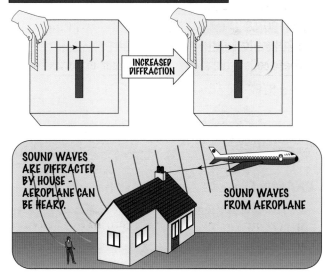

SOUND WAVES ARE DIFFRACTED BY HOUSE - AEROPLANE CAN BE HEARD.

SOUND WAVES FROM AEROPLANE

Diffraction Of Radio Waves

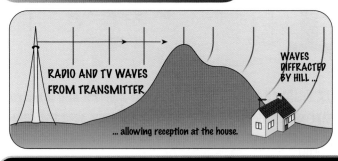

RADIO AND TV WAVES FROM TRANSMITTER

WAVES DIFFRACTED BY HILL ...

... allowing reception at the house.

Some places are able to pick up RADIO and TV WAVES even though HILLS OBSCURE THE SIGNAL from the DISTANT TRANSMITTER. Due to diffraction the quality of the received radio signals is maintained

Radio waves can also be picked up through reflection from the ionosphere, an electrically charged layer in the Earth's upper atmosphere.

Total Internal Reflection - When Refraction Becomes Reflection

When a ray of light travels from glass, 'perspex' or water into air some light is also reflected from the boundary. This can be best summarised in THREE stages. If the ANGLE OF INCIDENCE is ...

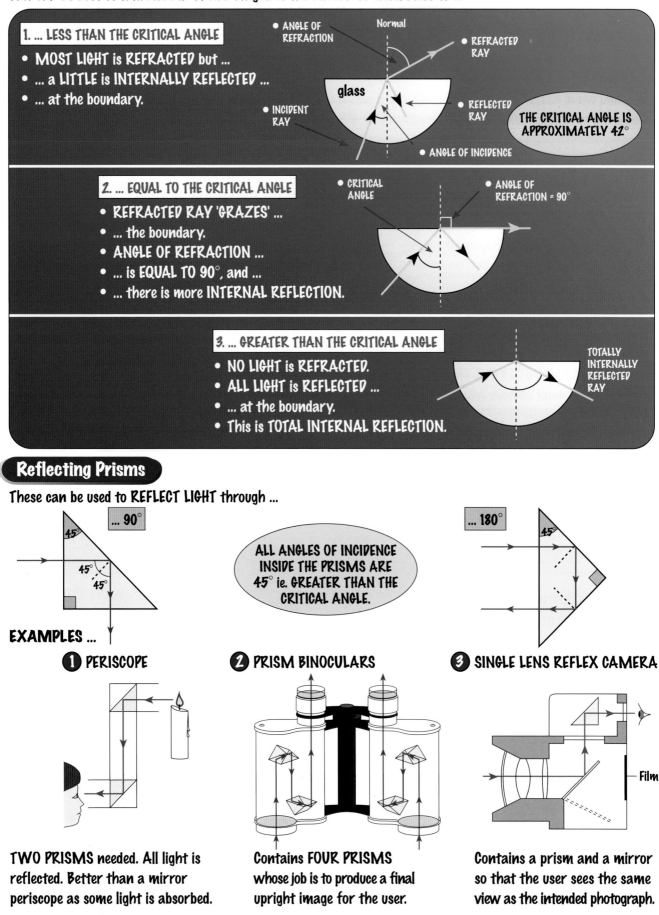

1. ... LESS THAN THE CRITICAL ANGLE

- MOST LIGHT is REFRACTED but ...
- ... a LITTLE is INTERNALLY REFLECTED ...
- ... at the boundary.

ANGLE OF REFRACTION

Normal

REFRACTED RAY

glass

REFLECTED RAY

INCIDENT RAY

THE CRITICAL ANGLE IS APPROXIMATELY 42°

ANGLE OF INCIDENCE

2. ... EQUAL TO THE CRITICAL ANGLE

- REFRACTED RAY 'GRAZES' ...
- ... the boundary.
- ANGLE OF REFRACTION ...
- ... is EQUAL TO 90°, and ...
- ... there is more INTERNAL REFLECTION.

CRITICAL ANGLE

ANGLE OF REFRACTION = 90°

3. ... GREATER THAN THE CRITICAL ANGLE

- NO LIGHT is REFRACTED.
- ALL LIGHT is REFLECTED ...
- ... at the boundary.
- This is TOTAL INTERNAL REFLECTION.

TOTALLY INTERNALLY REFLECTED RAY

Reflecting Prisms

These can be used to REFLECT LIGHT through ...

... 90°

45°
45°
45°

ALL ANGLES OF INCIDENCE INSIDE THE PRISMS ARE 45° ie. GREATER THAN THE CRITICAL ANGLE.

... 180°

45°

EXAMPLES ...

❶ PERISCOPE

❷ PRISM BINOCULARS

❸ SINGLE LENS REFLEX CAMERA

Film

TWO PRISMS needed. All light is reflected. Better than a mirror periscope as some light is absorbed.

Contains FOUR PRISMS whose job is to produce a final upright image for the user.

Contains a prism and a mirror so that the user sees the same view as the intended photograph.

Optical Fibres

An OPTICAL FIBRE is a long, flexible, transparent cable of very small diameter. Light is TOTALLY INTERNALLY REFLECTED along its length, staying inside the fibre, until it emerges from the other end.

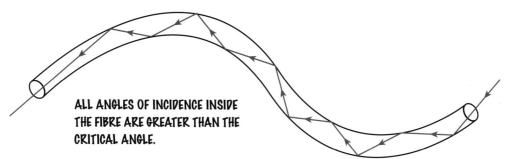

ALL ANGLES OF INCIDENCE INSIDE THE FIBRE ARE GREATER THAN THE CRITICAL ANGLE.

An important application of optical fibres is in telecommunications. Information can be transmitted via pulses of light or infra-red along optical fibres. This is more efficient than sending electrical signals through copper cables of the same diameter with less weakening of signal strength along the way.

The Endoscope

- Used for INTERNAL VIEWING OF THE HUMAN BODY.
- The endoscope consists of BUNDLES OF FIBRES, half of which ...
- ... TRANSMIT LIGHT to the part of the body being VIEWED ...
- ... and half of them TRANSMIT REFLECTED LIGHT BACK ...
- ... to form an IMAGE.

LIGHT REFLECTED BACK

PART OF BODY

LIGHT SENT DOWN

HIGHER TIER

Analogue And Digital Signals

- Analogue signals vary continually in amplitude and/or frequency.
  They are very similar to the sound waves of speech or music.

- Digital signals on the other hand do not vary and they have only two states, ON (1) or OFF (0).
  There are no inbetween states. The information is a series of pulses.

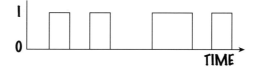

When analogue and digital signals are transmitted using optical fibres they become weaker.
They may also pick up additional signals or 'noise'. At selected intervals the transmitted signals have to be amplified.

The advantages of using digital signals instead of analogue signals for transmission are ...
- ... better quality, with no change in the signal information during transmission. Analogue signals become less and less like the original signal.
- ... more information can be transmitted in a given time.

Hooke's Law

Hooke's law deals with the extension (or compression) of an object when a force is applied to it.

A simple experiment to investigate how the EXTENSION of a spring (or metal wire) INCREASES as the APPLIED FORCE also INCREASES is shown below ...

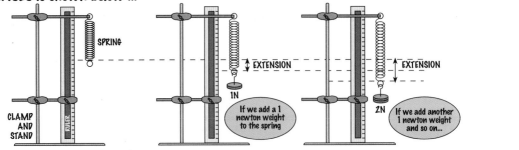

SPRING

EXTENSION

1N — If we add a 1 newton weight to the spring

EXTENSION

2N — If we add another 1 newton weight and so on...

CLAMP AND STAND — RULER

... and the results table would look like this ...

APPLIED FORCE (N)	1	2	3	4	5	6	7	8	9
EXTENSION (cm)	2.5	5.0	7.5	10.0	12.5	15.0	19.0	24.0	30.0

Below is the graph of EXTENSION against APPLIED FORCE for the results in the table above.
It has some important features.

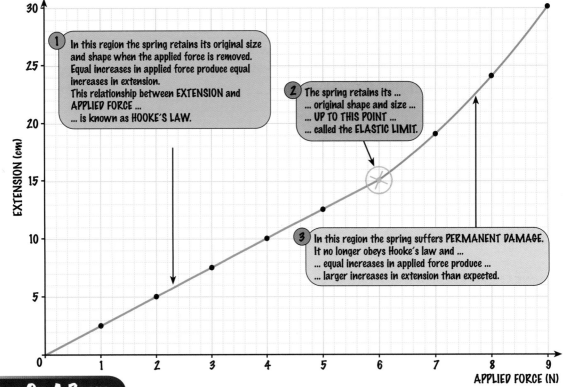

1 In this region the spring retains its original size and shape when the applied force is removed. Equal increases in applied force produce equal increases in extension.
This relationship between EXTENSION and APPLIED FORCE ...
... is known as HOOKE'S LAW.

2 The spring retains its ...
... original shape and size ...
... UP TO THIS POINT ...
... called the ELASTIC LIMIT.

3 In this region the spring suffers PERMANENT DAMAGE. It no longer obeys Hooke's law and ...
... equal increases in applied force produce ...
... larger increases in extension than expected.

EXTENSION (cm)

APPLIED FORCE (N)

Forces On A Beam

When a light beam is supported at each end the upward forces acting vary according to the position of a heavy object (load) placed on it.

1 When load, W, is in the middle, upward forces at both supports are equal (and equal to $\frac{W}{2}$)

2 When load, W, moves to the right, upward force on right-hand support increases while the one on the left decreases.

3 When load, W, moves to the left upward force on the left-hand support increases while the one on the right decreases.

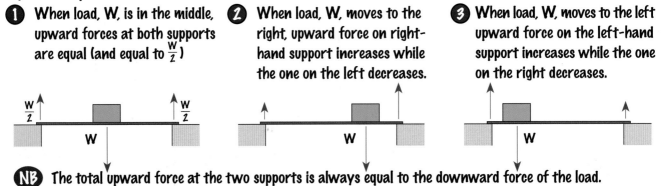

$\frac{W}{2}$ $\frac{W}{2}$

W

W

W

NB The total upward force at the two supports is always equal to the downward force of the load.

Gas Pressure

When a ball is blown up with air, many millions of tiny gas particles enter the ball. Once inside, the gas particles constantly hit the inside surface of the ball, exerting a force on its walls, because they are moving around very quickly and in random directions. This constant hitting of the inside surface creates GAS PRESSURE.

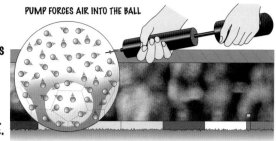

PUMP FORCES AIR INTO THE BALL

Crushing Can Experiment

Here on earth we live at the bottom of a 'sea of air'. All around us gas particles are constantly hitting us and everything else in their way. The ball above would have gas particles constantly hitting its outside surface. As this experiment shows these gas particles can have a devastating effect if they are not opposed.

Normally the number of gas particles hitting the inside of the can is the SAME as the number of particles hitting the outside of the can. They cancel each other out and there is no effect on the can.

AIR IS NOW REMOVED FROM THE CAN USING A PUMP.

TO VACUUM PUMP

As the air inside the can is removed the number of gas particles hitting the inside of the can is LESS THAN the number of particles hitting the outside of the can. This difference causes the can to 'collapse'.

HIGHER TIER

Pressure And Volume Relationship For A Gas

The gas syringe below contains a FIXED MASS OF GAS (amount of gas does not change) which is kept at a CONSTANT TEMPERATURE.

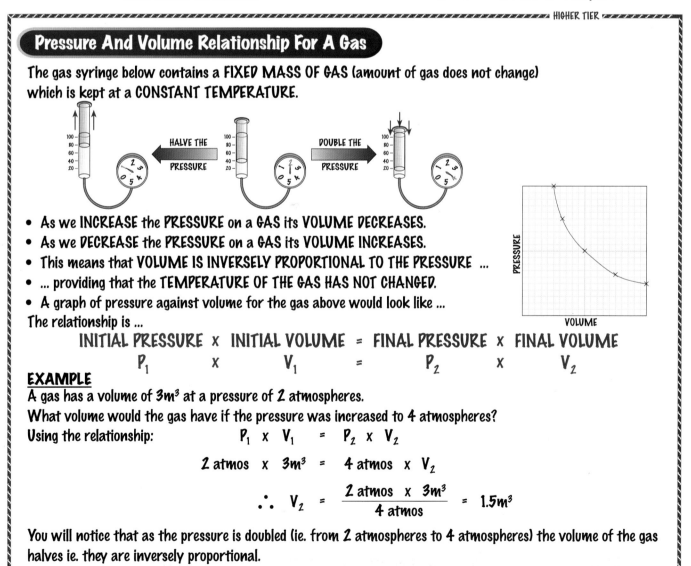

HALVE THE PRESSURE

DOUBLE THE PRESSURE

PRESSURE

VOLUME

- As we INCREASE the PRESSURE on a GAS its VOLUME DECREASES.
- As we DECREASE the PRESSURE on a GAS its VOLUME INCREASES.
- This means that VOLUME IS INVERSELY PROPORTIONAL TO THE PRESSURE ...
- ... providing that the TEMPERATURE OF THE GAS HAS NOT CHANGED.
- A graph of pressure against volume for the gas above would look like ...

The relationship is ...

INITIAL PRESSURE x INITIAL VOLUME = FINAL PRESSURE x FINAL VOLUME

$$P_1 \quad \times \quad V_1 \quad = \quad P_2 \quad \times \quad V_2$$

EXAMPLE

A gas has a volume of $3m^3$ at a pressure of 2 atmospheres.

What volume would the gas have if the pressure was increased to 4 atmospheres?

Using the relationship:

$$P_1 \times V_1 = P_2 \times V_2$$

$$2 \text{ atmos} \times 3m^3 = 4 \text{ atmos} \times V_2$$

$$\therefore V_2 = \frac{2 \text{ atmos} \times 3m^3}{4 \text{ atmos}} = 1.5m^3$$

You will notice that as the pressure is doubled (ie. from 2 atmospheres to 4 atmospheres) the volume of the gas halves ie. they are inversely proportional.

STATIC ELECTRICITY

Electrons can be transferred between different materials. Gaining electrons results in a negative charge while losing electrons results in a positive charge.

• The SAME CHARGES REPEL EACH OTHER and vice versa.

THE PHOTOCOPIER ...
(a) Copying plate is electrically charged.
(b) Image is projected onto the plate to leave an 'electrostatic impression'.
(c) This charged impression attracts the ink powder. This powder is then transferred from plate to paper and heated to fix the image.

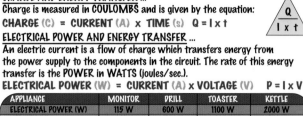

THE INKJET PRINTER ...
negatively charged ink droplets are deflected to where they are required by two charged plates across which a variable voltage is applied.

DISCHARGING UNSAFE STATIC ...
during refuelling of planes, the fuel gains electrons from the fuel pipe making the pipe POSITIVELY CHARGED and the fuel NEGATIVELY CHARGED. In order to prevent discharge and a spark, the plane is earthed or the tanker and the plane are connected via a copper wire.

> Earthing involves the equalisation of the electron imbalance between two bodies.

ENERGY IN CIRCUITS

CHARGE AND ENERGY TRANSFER ...
Charge is measured in COULOMBS and is given by the equation:

CHARGE (C) = CURRENT (A) x TIME (s) $Q = I \times t$

$$\dfrac{Q}{I \times t}$$

ELECTRICAL POWER AND ENERGY TRANSFER ...
An electric current is a flow of charge which transfers energy from the power supply to the components in the circuit. The rate of this energy transfer is the POWER in WATTS (joules/sec.).

ELECTRICAL POWER (W) = CURRENT (A) x VOLTAGE (V) $P = I \times V$

APPLIANCE	MONITOR	DRILL	TOASTER	KETTLE
ELECTRICAL POWER (W)	115 W	600 W	1100 W	2000 W
VOLTAGE (V)	230 V	230 V	230 V	230 V
CURRENT (A)	0.5 A	2.6 A	4.8 A	8.7 A

> ### ELECTRIC CURRENT IN METALS
> In metals an electric current is a flow of negatively charged electrons.
>
> ### ELECTRIC CURRENT IN MOLTEN AND DISSOLVED ELECTROLYTES
> Some substances produce ions when dissolved in water or melted. This allows them to conduct electricity due to NEGATIVE IONS MOVING TO THE +ve ELECTRODE and POSITIVE IONS MOVING TO THE -ve ELECTRODE, resulting in simple substances being released at the two electrodes.
>
> ### ENERGY TRANSFERRED
> ENERGY TRANSFERRED (J) = CURRENT (A) x VOLTAGE (V) x TIME (s)
> • Voltage is the energy transferred per unit charge passed. $E = I \times V \times t$

THE MOTOR EFFECT AND TRANSFORMERS

ELECTROMAGNETISM
• A magnetic field is formed around a wire carrying a current.

THE MOTOR EFFECT ...
• A current-carrying wire in a magnetic field experiences a force.
• The FORCE acting is always perpendicular to both the wire carrying the current and the magnetic field.

TRANSFORMERS ...
... 'step-up' and 'step-down' the voltage.

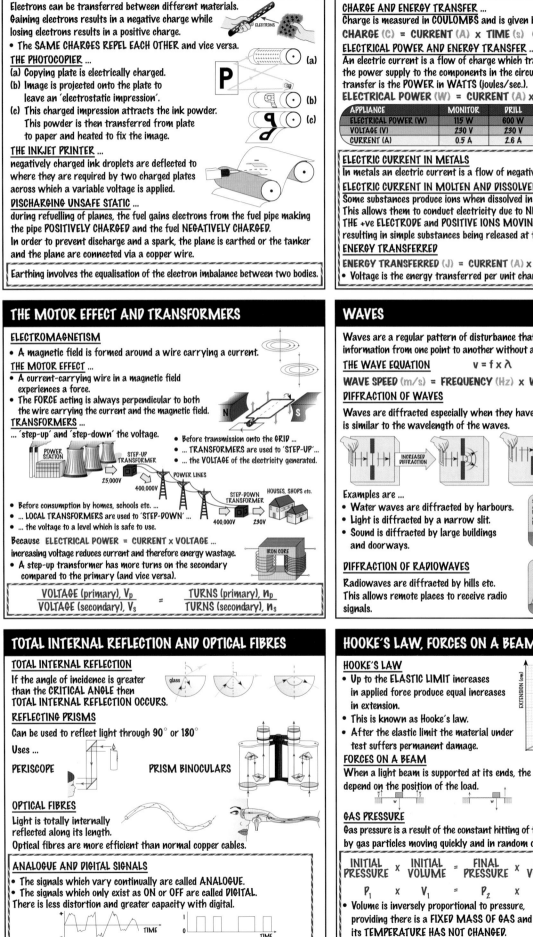

• Before transmission onto the GRID ...
• ... TRANSFORMERS are used to 'STEP-UP'...
• ... the VOLTAGE of the electricity generated.

POWER STATION 25,000V STEP-UP TRANSFORMER POWER LINES 400,000V

• Before consumption by homes, schools etc. ...
• ... LOCAL TRANSFORMERS are used to 'STEP-DOWN' ...
• ... the voltage to a level which is safe to use.

STEP-DOWN TRANSFORMER HOUSES, SHOPS etc. 400,000V 230V

Because ELECTRICAL POWER = CURRENT x VOLTAGE ...
increasing voltage reduces current and therefore energy wastage.
• A step-up transformer has more turns on the secondary compared to the primary (and vice versa).

IRON CORE

$$\frac{\text{VOLTAGE (primary), } V_p}{\text{VOLTAGE (secondary), } V_s} = \frac{\text{TURNS (primary), } n_p}{\text{TURNS (secondary), } n_s}$$

WAVES

Waves are a regular pattern of disturbance that transfer energy and information from one point to another without any transfer of matter.

THE WAVE EQUATION $v = f \times \lambda$

WAVE SPEED (m/s) = FREQUENCY (Hz) x WAVELENGTH (m)

$$\dfrac{v}{f \times \lambda}$$

DIFFRACTION OF WAVES
Waves are diffracted especially when they have long wavelengths or the gap is similar to the wavelength of the waves.

INCREASED DIFFRACTION   INCREASED DIFFRACTION

Examples are ...
• Water waves are diffracted by harbours.
• Light is diffracted by a narrow slit.
• Sound is diffracted by large buildings and doorways.

SOUND WAVES ARE DIFFRACTED BY HOUSE. AEROPLANE CAN BE HEARD   SOUND WAVES FROM AEROPLANE

DIFFRACTION OF RADIOWAVES
Radiowaves are diffracted by hills etc. This allows remote places to receive radio signals.

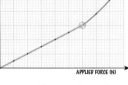
RADIO AND TV WAVES FROM TRANSMITTER   WAVES DIFFRACTED BY HILL
... allowing reception at the house.

TOTAL INTERNAL REFLECTION AND OPTICAL FIBRES

TOTAL INTERNAL REFLECTION
If the angle of incidence is greater than the CRITICAL ANGLE then TOTAL INTERNAL REFLECTION OCCURS.

glass

REFLECTING PRISMS
Can be used to reflect light through 90° or 180°

Uses ...

PERISCOPE   PRISM BINOCULARS

OPTICAL FIBRES
Light is totally internally reflected along its length.
Optical fibres are more efficient than normal copper cables.

> ### ANALOGUE AND DIGITAL SIGNALS
> • The signals which vary continually are called ANALOGUE.
> • The signals which only exist as ON or OFF are called DIGITAL. There is less distortion and greater capacity with digital.
>
> TIME   TIME

HOOKE'S LAW, FORCES ON A BEAM AND GAS PRESSURE

HOOKE'S LAW
• Up to the ELASTIC LIMIT increases in applied force produce equal increases in extension.
• This is known as Hooke's law.
• After the elastic limit the material under test suffers permanent damage.

EXTENSION (cm)   APPLIED FORCE (N)

FORCES ON A BEAM
When a light beam is supported at its ends, the upward forces acting on it depend on the position of the load.

GAS PRESSURE
Gas pressure is a result of the constant hitting of the inside surface of a container by gas particles moving quickly and in random directions.

> | INITIAL PRESSURE | x | INITIAL VOLUME | = | FINAL PRESSURE | x | FINAL VOLUME |
> |---|---|---|---|---|---|---|
> | P_1 | x | V_1 | = | P_2 | x | V_2 |
>
> • Volume is inversely proportional to pressure, providing there is a FIXED MASS OF GAS and its TEMPERATURE HAS NOT CHANGED.

PRESSURE   VOLUME

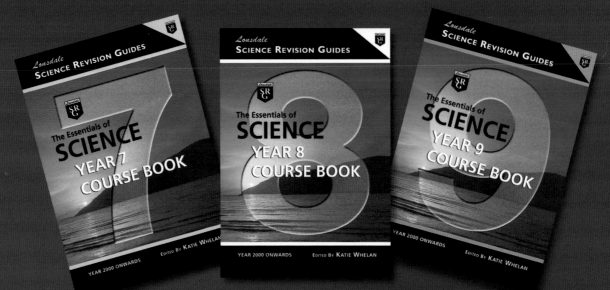
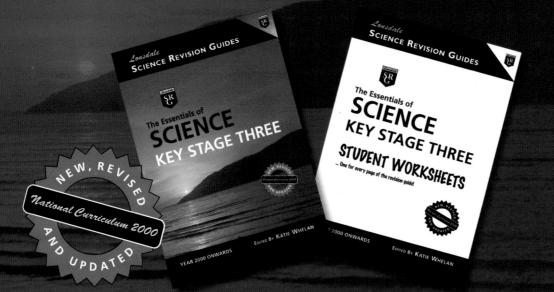